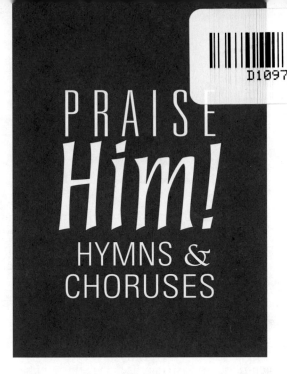

PRAISE Him!
HYMNS & CHORUSES

This collection of traditional hymns and choruses contains songs appropriate for the home, school, and church. Heartfelt singing of psalms, hymns, and spiritual songs provides Christians a way to praise God in obedience to Scripture.

Make a joyful noise unto the Lord, all ye lands. Serve the Lord with gladness: come before his presence with **singing.**
—Ps. 100:1–2

Speaking to yourselves in **psalms** *and* **hymns** *and* **spiritual songs,** *singing and making melody in your heart to the Lord.*
—Eph. 5:19

A Beka Book® Pensacola, FL 32523-9100
an affiliated ministry of PENSACOLA CHRISTIAN COLLEGE®

Why Sing Hymns?

*"Our youth are growing up not
ever learning the hymns."*
—Concerned Parent

The trend today is to replace traditional hymns with contemporary praise choruses. But is this trend good for young people? Youth today need the strong focus on doctrine that the hymns and choruses in this hymnal provide. Hymns present a clear expression of the knowledge of God, and they teach Biblical truth as Scripture admonishes:

> *Let the word of Christ dwell in you richly in all wisdom; **teaching** and **admonishing** one another in psalms and hymns and spiritual songs.*
>
> —Col. 3:16

However, most contemporary praise choruses lack this emphasis. For example, a Muslim can sing many contemporary praise choruses and never utter a contradiction of his faith because praise choruses tend to focus on our affections for God rather than on doctrinal truth. In contrast, a Muslim cannot sing a Christian hymn without professing doctrine that contradicts his Islamic faith. Furthermore, contemporary praise choruses often omit the identity of the God to Whom we sing, and they are so vague they could be sung to any false god. Good gospel choruses play an appropriate role in our worship, but they cannot take the place of hymns rich in doctrine.

To discard hymns is not only unwise, but it is dangerous, for the identification and character of our Christian faith depends upon doctrinal distinctions. By singing traditional hymns that are permeated with doctrinal truth, we help protect younger generations against the indictment in Hosea 4:1:

> *". . . there is no truth, nor mercy, nor knowledge of God in the land."*

Praise Him! Hymns & Choruses

Staff Credits
Compiled and edited by Brian Ashbaugh, Eduardo Inke, Andy Cole, Jesse Becker, Greg Soule
Cover design by Steven Haught
Production Artist: Thad Lund

A Beka Book, a Christian textbook ministry affiliated with Pensacola Christian College, is designed to meet the need for Christian textbooks and teaching aids. The purpose of this publishing ministry is to help Christian schools reach children and young people for the Lord and train them in the Christian way of life.

A Mighty Fortress Is Our God

Martin Luther
Trans. by Frederick H. Hedge

Martin Luther

1. A might-y for-tress is our God, A bul-wark nev-er fail-ing;
2. Did we in our own strength con-fide, Our striv-ing would be los-ing;
3. And though this world, with dev-ils filled, Should threat-en to un-do us,
4. That word a-bove all earth-ly powers, No thanks to them, a-bid-eth;

Our help-er He, a-mid the flood Of mor-tal ills pre-vail-ing:
Were not the right Man on our side, The Man of God's own choos-ing:
We will not fear, for God hath willed His truth to tri-umph through us:
The Spir-it and the gifts are ours Thro' Him who with us sid-eth:

For still our an-cient foe Doth seek to work us woe; His craft and power are
Dost ask who that may be? Christ Je-sus, it is He, Lord Sa-ba-oth, His
The Prince of Dark-ness grim— We trem-ble not for him; His rage we can en-
Let goods and kin-dred go, This mor-tal life al-so; The bod-y they may

great, And, armed with cru-el hate, On earth is not his e-qual.
name, From age to age the same, And He must win the bat-tle.
dure, For lo, his doom is sure, One lit-tle word shall fell him.
kill: God's truth a-bid-eth still, His king-dom is for-ev-er.

2

Blessed Be the Name

W. H. Clark
Chorus by Ralph E. Hudson

Ralph E. Hudson
Arr. by William J. Kirkpatrick

1. All praise to Him who reigns a - bove In maj - es - ty su - preme
2. His name a - bove all names shall stand, Ex - alt - ed more and more,
3. Re - deem - er, Sav - ior, Friend of man Once ru - ined by the fall,
4. His name shall be the Coun - sel - or, The might - y Prince of Peace,

Who gave His Son for man to die, That He might man re - deem!
At God the Fa - ther's own right hand, Where an - gel - hosts a - dore.
Thou hast de - vised sal - va - tion's plan, For Thou hast died for all.
Of all earth's king - doms Con - quer - or, Whose reign shall nev - er cease.

Chorus

Bless - ed be the name, bless - ed be the name, Bless - ed

be the name of the Lord! Bless - ed be the name,

bless - ed be the name, Bless - ed be the name of the Lord!

Great Is Thy Faithfulness

3

Thomas O. Chisholm

William M. Runyan

1. Great is Thy faith-ful-ness, O God my Fa-ther, There is no shad-ow of
2. Sum-mer and win-ter, and spring-time and har-vest, Sun, moon and stars in their
3. Par-don for sin and a peace that en-dur-eth, Thy own dear presence to

turn-ing with Thee; Thou chang-est not, Thy com-pas-sions they fail not;
cours-es a-bove Join with all na-ture in man-i-fold wit-ness
cheer and to guide; Strength for to-day and bright hope for to-mor-row,

Refrain

As Thou hast been Thou for-ev-er wilt be.
To Thy great faith-ful-ness, mer-cy and love. Great is Thy faith-ful-ness!
Bless-ings all mine, with ten thou-sand be-side!

Great is Thy faith-ful-ness! Morn-ing by morn-ing new mer-cies I see; All I have

need-ed Thy hand hath pro-vid-ed— Great is Thy faith-ful-ness, Lord, un-to me!

4

How Great Thou Art!

Stuart K. Hine (1899–1989)

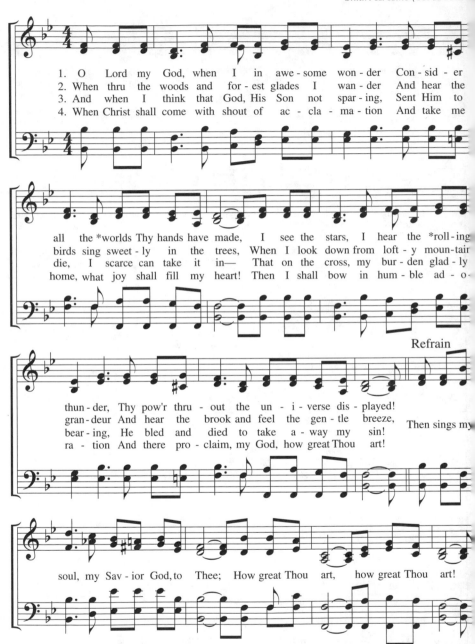

1. O Lord my God, when I in awe-some won-der Con-sid-er
2. When thru the woods and for-est glades I wan-der And hear the
3. And when I think that God, His Son not spar-ing, Sent Him to
4. When Christ shall come with shout of ac-cla-ma-tion And take me

all the *worlds Thy hands have made, I see the stars, I hear the *roll-ing
birds sing sweet-ly in the trees, When I look down from loft-y moun-tain
die, I scarce can take it in— That on the cross, my bur-den glad-ly
home, what joy shall fill my heart! Then I shall bow in hum-ble ad-o-

Refrain

thun-der, Thy pow'r thru-out the un-i-verse dis-played!
gran-deur And hear the brook and feel the gen-tle breeze,   Then sings my
bear-ing, He bled and died to take a-way my sin!
ra-tion And there pro-claim, my God, how great Thou art!

soul, my Sav-ior God, to Thee; How great Thou art, how great Thou art!

* Author's original words are "works" and "mighty."

Then sings my soul, my Sav-ior God, to Thee; How great Thou art, how great Thou art!

Holy, Holy, Holy!

5

Reginald Heber

John B. Dykes

1. Ho - ly, Ho - ly, Ho - ly! Lord God Al - might - y! Ear - ly in the
2. Ho - ly, Ho - ly, Ho - ly! All the saints a - dore Thee, Cast - ing down their
3. Ho - ly, Ho - ly, Ho - ly! Tho' the dark-ness hide Thee, Tho' the eye of
4. Ho - ly, Ho - ly, Ho - ly! Lord God Al - might - y! All Thy works shall

morn - ing our song shall rise to Thee; Ho - ly, Ho - ly, Ho - ly!
gold - en crowns a - round the glass - y sea; Cher - u - bim and ser - a-phim
sin - ful man Thy glo - ry may not see, On - ly Thou art ho - ly;
praise Thy name, in earth, and sky, and sea; Ho - ly, Ho - ly, Ho - ly!

Mer - ci - ful and Might - y! God in Three Per - sons, bless - ed Trin - i - ty!
fall - ing down be - fore Thee, Which wert and art, and ev - er-more shall be.
there is none be - side Thee Per - fect in pow'r, in love, and pu - ri - ty.
Mer - ci - ful and Might - y! God in Three Per - sons, bless - ed Trin - i - ty!

6   For the Beauty of the Earth

Folliott S. Pierpoint

Arr. from Conrad Kocher

1. For the beau-ty of the earth, For the glo-ry of the skies,
2. For the beau-ty of each hour Of the day and of the night,
3. For the joy of hu-man love, Broth-er, sis-ter, par-ent, child,
4. For Thy Church that ev-er-more Lift-eth ho-ly hands a-bove,

For the love which from our birth O-ver and a-round us lies,
Hill and vale, and tree and flow'r, Sun and moon, and stars of light,
Friends on earth, and friends a-bove, For all gen-tle thoughts and mild,
Off-'ring up on ev'ry shore Her pure sac-ri-fice of love,

Lord of all, to Thee we raise This our hymn of grate-ful praise.

7   O God, Our Help in Ages Past

Isaac Watts

Ascribed to William Croft

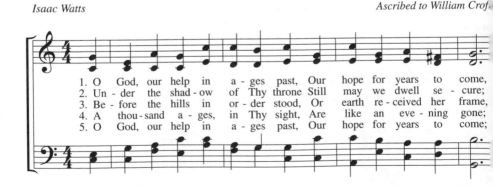

1. O God, our help in a-ges past, Our hope for years to come,
2. Un-der the shad-ow of Thy throne Still may we dwell se-cure;
3. Be-fore the hills in or-der stood, Or earth re-ceived her frame,
4. A thou-sand a-ges, in Thy sight, Are like an eve-ning gone;
5. O God, our help in a-ges past, Our hope for years to come;

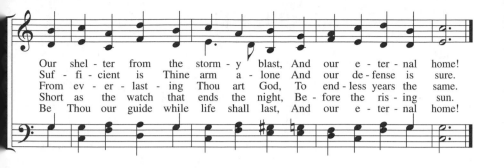

Our shel - ter from the storm - y blast, And our e - ter - nal home!
Suf - fi - cient is Thine arm a - lone And our de - fense is sure.
From ev - er - last - ing Thou art God, To end - less years the same.
Short as the watch that ends the night, Be - fore the ris - ing sun.
Be Thou our guide while life shall last, And our e - ter - nal home!

O Worship the King

8

Robert Grant

J. Michael Haydn

1. O wor - ship the King, all - glo - rious a - bove, O grate - ful - ly
2. O tell of His might, O sing of His grace, Whose robe is the
3. Thy boun - ti - ful care what tongue can re - cite? It breathes in the
4. Frail chil - dren of dust, and fee - ble as frail, In Thee do we

sing His pow - er and His love; Our Shield and De - fend - er, the
light, whose can - o - py space. His char - iots of wrath the deep
air, it shines in the light, It streams from the hills, it de -
trust, nor find Thee to fail; Thy mer - cies how ten - der! how

An - cient of Days, Pa - vil - ioned in splen-dor, and gird - ed with praise.
thun - der - clouds form, And dark is His path on the wings of the storm.
scends to the plain, And sweet - ly dis - tills in the dew and the rain.
firm to the end! Our Mak - er, De - fend - er, Re - deem - er and Friend.

9 This Is My Father's World

Maltbie D. Babcock   *Franklin L. Sheppard*

1. This is my Fa-ther's world, And to my lis-tening ears All
2. This is my Fa-ther's world, The birds their car-ols raise, The
3. This is my Fa-ther's world, O let me ne'er for-get That

na-ture sings, and round me rings The mu-sic of the spheres.
morn-ing light, the lil-y white, De-clare their Mak-er's praise.
though the wrong seems oft so strong, God is the Rul-er yet.

This is my Fa-ther's world: I rest me in the thought Of
This is my Fa-ther's world: He shines in all that's fair; In the
This is my Fa-ther's world: The bat-tle is not done; Je-

rocks and trees, of skies and seas— His hand the won-ders wrought.
rus-tling grass I hear Him pass, He speaks to me ev-'ry-where.
sus who died shall be sat-is-fied, And earth and heav-en be one.

A Shelter in the Time of Storm

10

Vernon J. Charlesworth
Adapted by Ira D. Sankey

Ira D. Sankey

1. The Lord's our Rock, in Him we hide, A shel-ter in the time of storm;
2. A shade by day, de-fense by night, A shel-ter in the time of storm;
3. The rag-ing storms may round us beat, A shel-ter in the time of storm;
4. O Rock di-vine, O Ref-uge dear, A shel-ter in the time of storm;

Se-cure what-ev-er ill be-tide, A shel-ter in the time of storm.
No fears a-larm, no foes af-fright, A shel-ter in the time of storm.
We'll nev-er leave our safe re-treat, A shel-ter in the time of storm.
Be Thou our help-er ev-er near, A shel-ter in the time of storm.

Refrain

Oh, Je-sus is a Rock in a wea-ry land, A wea-ry land, a wea-ry land;

Oh, Je-sus is a Rock in a wea-ry land, A shel-ter in the time of storm.

All Hail the Power

E. Perronet

Oliver Holden

1. All hail the pow'r of Je - sus' name! Let an - gels pros - trate fall;
2. Ye cho - sen seed of Is - rael's race, Ye ran - somed from the fall,
3. Let ev - 'ry kin - dred, ev - 'ry tribe On this ter - res - trial ball,
4. O that with yon - der sa - cred throng We at His feet may fall!

Bring forth the roy - al di - a - dem, And crown Him Lord of all,
Hail Him who saves you by His grace, And crown Him Lord of all,
To Him all maj - es - ty as - cribe, And crown Him Lord of all,
We'll join the ev - er - las - ting song, And crown Him Lord of all,

Bring forth the roy - al di - a - dem, And crown Him Lord of all!
Hail Him who saves you by His grace, And crown Him Lord of all!
To Him all maj - es - ty as - cribe, And crown Him Lord of all!
We'll join the ev - er - las - ting song, And crown Him Lord of all!

12 Jesus the Very Thought of Thee

Attrib. to Bernard of Clairvaux
Trans. by Edward Caswall

John B. Dykes

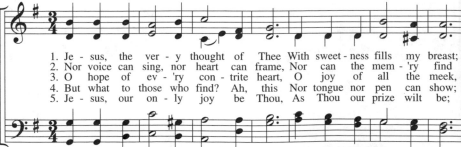

1. Je - sus, the ver - y thought of Thee With sweet - ness fills my breast;
2. Nor voice can sing, nor heart can frame, Nor can the mem - 'ry find
3. O hope of ev - 'ry con - trite heart, O joy of all the meek,
4. But what to those who find? Ah, this Nor tongue nor pen can show;
5. Je - sus, our on - ly joy be Thou, As Thou our prize wilt be;

But sweet-er far Thy face to see And in Thy pres - ence rest.
A sweet-er sound than Thy blest name, O Sav - ior of man - kind.
To those who fall how kind Thou art! How good to those who seek!
The love of Je - sus, what it is None but His loved ones know.
Je - sus, be Thou our glo - ry now And thru e - ter - ni - ty.

Fairest Lord Jesus 13

From the German
17th Century

Silesian Folksong
Arr. by James Hopkirk

1. Fair - est Lord Je - sus, Rul - er of all na - ture,
2. Fair are the mead - ows, Fair - er still the wood - lands,
3. Fair is the sun - shine, Fair - er still the moon - light,
4. All fair - est beau - ty Heav - en - ly and earth - ly,

O Thou of God and man the Son; Thee will I cher - ish,
Robed in the bloom - ing garb of spring; Je - sus is fair - er,
And fair the twink - ling, star - ry host; Je - sus shines bright - er,
Won - drous - ly, Je - sus, is found in Thee; None can be near - er,

Thee will I hon - or, Thou my soul's glo - ry, joy, and crown.
Je - sus is pur - er, Who makes the woe - ful heart to sing.
Je - sus shines pur - er, Than all the an - gels heaven can boast.
fair - er or dear - er, Than Thou, my Sav - iour, art to me.

14   He Keeps Me Singing

Luther B. Bridgers   *Luther B. Bridgers*

1. There's with-in my heart a mel-o-dy Je-sus whis-pers
2. All my life was wrecked by sin and strife, Dis-cord filled my
3. Feast-ing on the rich-es of His grace, Rest-ing 'neath His
4. Though some-times He leads through wa-ters deep, Tri-als fall a-
5. Soon He's com-ing back to wel-come me Far be-yond the

sweet and low, "Fear not, I am with thee, peace be still,"
heart with pain; Je-sus swept a-cross the bro-ken strings,
shelt-ering wing, Al-ways look-ing on His smil-ing face—
cross the way, Though some-times the path seems rough and steep,
star-ry sky; I shall wing my flight to worlds un-known,

Refrain

In all of life's ebb and flow.
Stirred the slum-bering chords a-gain.
That is why I shout and sing.   Je-sus, Je-sus, Je-sus— Sweet-est
See His foot-prints all the way.
I shall reign with Him on high.

name I know, Fills my ev-ery long-ing, Keeps me sing-ing as I go.

Ivory Palaces

Henry Barraclough   *Henry Barraclough*

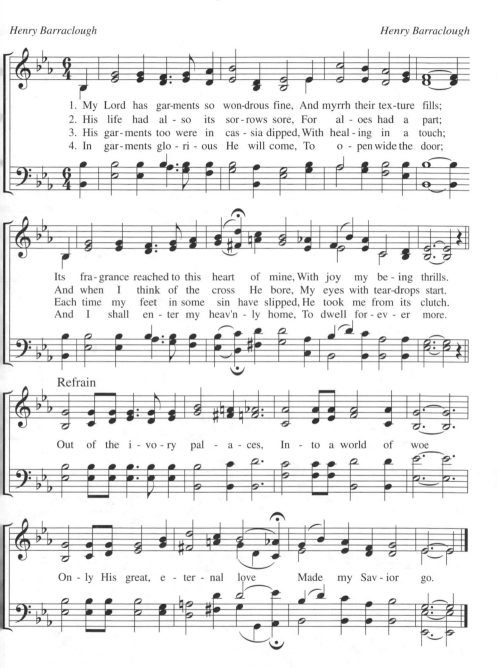

1. My Lord has gar-ments so won-drous fine, And myrrh their tex-ture fills;
2. His life had al - so its sor-rows sore, For al - oes had a part;
3. His gar-ments too were in cas - sia dipped, With heal - ing in a touch;
4. In gar-ments glo - ri - ous He will come, To o - pen wide the door;

Its fra-grance reached to this heart of mine, With joy my be - ing thrills.
And when I think of the cross He bore, My eyes with tear-drops start.
Each time my feet in some sin have slipped, He took me from its clutch.
And I shall en - ter my heav'n - ly home, To dwell for - ev - er more.

Refrain

Out of the i - vo - ry pal - a - ces, In - to a world of woe

On - ly His great, e - ter - nal love Made my Sav - ior go.

16   Still Sweeter Every Day

W. C. Martin   *C. Austin Miles*

1. To Je - sus ev - ery day I find my heart is clos - er drawn; He's
2. His glo - ry broke up - on me when I saw Him from a - far; He's
3. My heart is some - times heav - y, but He comes with sweet re - lief; He

fair - er than the glo - ry of the gold and pur - ple dawn; He's
fair - er than the lil - y, bright - er than the morn - ing star; He
folds me to His bos - om when I droop with blight - ing grief; I

all my fan - cy pic - tures in its fair - est dreams, and more; Each day He
fills and sat - is - fies my long - ing spir - it o'er and o'er; Each day He
love the Christ who all my bur - dens in His bod - y bore; Each day He

Refrain

grows still sweet - er than He was the day be - fore.
The half

The half can - not be fan -

can - not be fan - cied   this side

cied on this side the gold - en shore, The half can - not be fan -

the gold - en shore; Oh, there
cied on this side the gold - en shore; Oh, there He'll be still sweet -

He'll be still sweet - er than He ev - er was be - fore.
er than He ev - er was be-fore, than He ev - er was be - fore.

O for a Thousand Tongues to Sing   17

Carl G. Glazer
Charles Wesley   *Arr. by Lowell Mason*

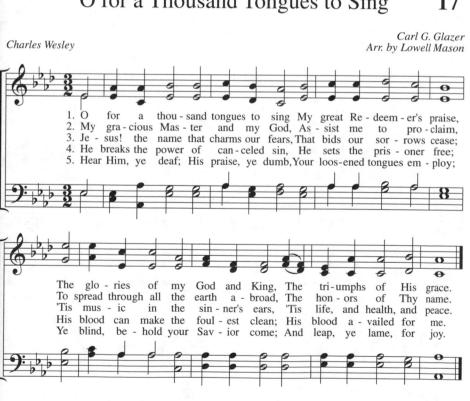

1. O for a thou - sand tongues to sing My great Re - deem - er's praise,
2. My gra - cious Mas - ter and my God, As - sist me to pro - claim,
3. Je - sus! the name that charms our fears, That bids our sor - rows cease;
4. He breaks the power of can - celed sin, He sets the pris - oner free;
5. Hear Him, ye deaf; His praise, ye dumb, Your loos-ened tongues em - ploy;

The glo - ries of my God and King, The tri - umphs of His grace.
To spread through all the earth a - broad, The hon - ors of Thy name.
'Tis mus - ic in the sin - ner's ears, 'Tis life, and health, and peace.
His blood can make the foul - est clean; His blood a - vailed for me.
Ye blind, be - hold your Sav - ior come; And leap, ye lame, for joy.

18   Jesus Is the Sweetest Name I Know

Lela Long   *Lela Long*

1. There have been names that I have loved to hear, But nev - er has there
2. There is no name in earth or heav'n a - bove, That we should give such
3. And some day I shall see Him face to face To thank and praise Him

been a name so dear To this heart of mine, as the name di - vine, The
hon - or and such love, As the bless-ed name, let us all ac - claim, That
for His won-drous grace, Which He gave to me, when He made me free, The

Chorus

pre - cious, pre-cious name of Je - sus.
won - drous, glo - rious name of Je - sus.   Je - sus is the sweet-est name I
bless - ed Son of God called Je - sus.

know, And He's just the same as His love-ly name, And that's the rea - son

rall.

why I love Him so; Oh, Je - sus is the sweet-est name I know.

Take the Name of Jesus with You

Lydia Baxter

William H. Doane

1. Take the name of Je - sus with you, Child of sor - row and of woe—
2. Take the name of Je - sus ev - er As a shield from ev - ery snare;
3. Oh, the pre - cious name of Je - sus; How it thrills our souls with joy,
4. At the name of Je - sus bow - ing, Fall - ing pros - trate at His feet,

It will joy and com - fort give you, Take it then wher - e'er you go.
If temp - ta - tions 'round you gath - er, Breathe that ho - ly name in prayer.
When His lov - ing arms re - ceive us And His songs our tongues em - ploy!
King of kings in heaven we'll crown Him When our jour - ney is com - plete.

Refrain

Pre - cious name, Oh, how sweet! Hope of earth and joy of heav'n,
Pre - cious name Oh, how sweet!

Pre - cious name, Oh, how sweet— Hope of earth and joy of heav'n.
Pre - cious name, Oh, how sweet, how sweet—

20   As with Gladness Men of Old

William C. Dix

Conrad Koche

1. As with glad-ness men of old Did the guid-ing star be-hold—
2. As with joy-ful steps they sped To that low-ly man-ger-bed,
3. As they of-fered gifts most rare At that man-ger rude and bare,
4. Ho-ly Je-sus, ev-'ry day Keep us in the nar-row way;

As with joy they hailed its light, Lead-ing on-ward, beam-ing bright—
There to bend the knee be-fore Him whom heav'n and earth a-dore,
So may we with ho-ly joy, Pure and free from sin's al-loy,
And, when earth-ly things are past, Bring our ran-somed souls at last

So, most gra-cious Lord, may we Ev-er-more be led to Thee.
So may we with will-ing feet Ev-er seek Thy mer-cy-seat.
All our cost-liest treas-ures bring, Christ, to Thee, our heav'n-ly King.
Where they need no star to guide, Where no clouds Thy glo-ry hide.

21   While Shepherds Watched Their Flocks

Nahum Tate

George F. Hand

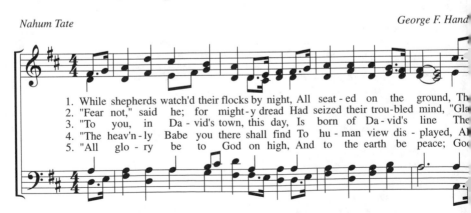

1. While shepherds watch'd their flocks by night, All seat-ed on the ground, Th
2. "Fear not," said he; for might-y dread Had seized their trou-bled mind, "Gla
3. "To you, in Da-vid's town, this day, Is born of Da-vid's line The
4. "The heav'n-ly Babe you there shall find To hu-man view dis-played, A
5. "All glo-ry be to God on high, And to the earth be peace; Go

Away in a Manger

22

Martin Luther

Carl Mueller

23 Angels, from the Realms of Glory

James Montgomery

Henry Smar

1. An - gels, from the realms of glo - ry, Wing your flight o'er
2. Shep-herds, in the fields a - bid - ing, Watch - ing o'er your
3. Sag - es, leave your con - tem - pla - tions, Bright - er vi - sions
4. Saints, be - fore the al - tar bend - ing, Watch - ing long in

all the earth; Ye who sang cre - a - tion's sto - ry,
flocks by night, God with man is now re - sid - ing,
beam a - far; Seek the great De - sire of na - tions,
hope and fear, Sud - den - ly the Lord, de - scend - ing,

Now pro - claim Mes - si - ah's birth: Come and wor - ship,
Yon - der shines the in - fant Light: Come and wor - ship,
Ye have seen His na - tal star: Come and wor - ship,
In His tem - ple shall ap - pear: Come and wor - ship,

come and wor - ship, Wor - ship Christ, the new - born King!
come and wor - ship, Wor - ship Christ, the new - born King!
come and wor - ship, Wor - ship Christ, the new - born King!
come and wor - ship, Wor - ship Christ, the new - born King!

The First Noel

Old English Carol

In Sandys' Christmas Carols

1. The first No - el the an - gel did say Was to cer - tain poor
2. They look - ed up and saw a star Shin-ing in the
3. And by the light of that same star, Three Wise Men
4. This star drew nigh to the north - west; O'er Beth - le -
5. Then en - tered in those Wise Men three, Fell rev - erent-
6. Then let us all with one ac - cord Sing prais - es

shepherds in fields as they lay; In fields where they lay keep - ing their
east be - yond them far, And to the earth it gave great
came from coun - try far; To seek for a king was their in -
hem it took its rest; And there it did both stop and
ly up - on their knee, And of - fered there in His pres -
to our heav - en - ly Lord, That hath made heaven and earth of

sheep, On a cold win-ter's night that was so deep.
light, And so it con - tin - ued both day and night.
tent, And to fol - low the star wher - ev - er it went.
stay, Right o - ver the place where Je - sus lay.
ence, Their gold, and myrrh, and frank - in - cense.
nought, And with His blood man - kind hath bought.

Refrain

No - el, No -

el, No - el, No - el, Born is the King of Is - ra - el.

Hark, the Herald Angels Sing

Felix Mendelssohn
Adapted by William H. Cummings

Charles Wesley

1. Hark, the her - ald an - gels sing, "Glo - ry to the new - born King;
2. Christ, by high - est heaven a - dored; Christ, the ev - er - last - ing Lord!
3. Hail, the heaven-born Prince of Peace! Hail, the Sun of Right - eous - ness!

Peace on earth, and mer - cy mild, God and sin - ners rec - on - ciled!"
Late in time be - hold Him come, Off - spring of the vir - gin's womb.
Light and life to all He brings, Risen with heal - ing in His wings.

Joy - ful, all ye na - tions, rise, Join the tri - umph of the skies;
Veiled in flesh the God - head see; Hail th' in - car - nate De - i - ty,
Mild He lays His glo - ry by, Born that man no more may die,

With th' an - gel - ic host pro - claim, "Christ is born in Beth - le - hem!"
Pleased as man with men to dwell, Je - sus, our Em - man - u - el!
Born to raise the sons of earth, Born to give them sec - ond birth.

Hark, the her - ald an - gels sing, "Glo - ry to the new - born King."

It Came upon the Midnight Clear

Edmund H. Sears

Richard S. Willis

1. It came up-on the mid-night clear, That glo-rious song of old,
2. Still through the clo-ven skies they come, With peace-ful wings un-furled,
3. And ye, be-neath life's crush-ing load, Whose forms are bend-ing low,
4. For lo, the days are has-tening on, By proph-et-bards fore-told,

From an-gels bend-ing near the earth To touch their harps of gold:
And still their heav'n-ly mu-sic floats O'er all the wea-ry world:
Who toil a-long the climb-ing way With pain-ful steps and slow,
When, with the ev-er-cir-cling years, Comes round the age of gold:

"Peace on the earth, good-will to men, From heav'n's all-gra-cious King":
A-bove its sad and low-ly plains They bend on hov-ering wing:
Look now! for glad and gold-en hours Come swift-ly on the wing;
When peace shall o-ver all the earth Its an-cient splen-dors fling,

The world in sol-emn still-ness lay To hear the an-gels sing.
And ev-er o'er its Ba-bel sounds The bless-ed an-gels sing.
O rest be-side the wea-ry road, And hear the an-gels sing.
And the whole world give back the song Which now the an-gels sing.

27 Joy to the World

Isaac Watts
Based on Psalm 98

George F. Handel

1. Joy to the world! the Lord is come; Let earth re-
2. Joy to the earth! the Sav - iour reigns; Let men their
3. No more let sins and sor - rows grow, Nor thorns in-
4. He rules the world with truth and grace, And makes the

ceive her King; Let ev - ery heart pre - pare Him
songs em - ploy; While fields and floods, rocks, hills, and
fest the ground; He comes to make His bless - ings
na - tions prove The glo - ries of His right - eous -

room, And heaven and na - ture sing, And heaven and na - ture
plains, Re - peat the sound-ing joy, Re - peat the sound-ing
flow Far as the curse is found, Far as the curse is
ness, And won-ders of His love, And won-ders of His

1. And heaven and na-ture sing,

1. And

sing, And heaven, and heaven and na - ture sing.
joy, Re - peat, re - peat the sound-ing joy.
found, Far as, far as the curse is found.
love, And won - ders, won - ders of His love.

heaven and na - ture sing,

O Come, All Ye Faithful

Anon. Latin
Trans. by Frederick Oakeley

John Wade's Cantus Diversi

1. O come, all ye faith - ful, joy - ful and tri - um - phant, O
2. Sing, choirs of an - gels, sing in ex - ul - ta - tion, O
3. Yea, Lord, we greet Thee, born this hap - py morn - ing,

come ye, O come ye to Beth - le - hem! Come and be - hold Him,
sing, all ye bright hosts of heav'n a - bove! Glo - ry to God, all
Je - sus, to Thee be all glo - ry giv'n; Word of the Fa - ther,

Refrain

born the King of an - gels!
glo - ry in the high - est! O come, let us a - dore Him, O come, let us a -
now in flesh ap - pear - ing!

dore Him, O come, let us a - dore Him, Christ the Lord!

O Little Town of Bethlehem

Phillips Brooks   *Lewis H. Redner*

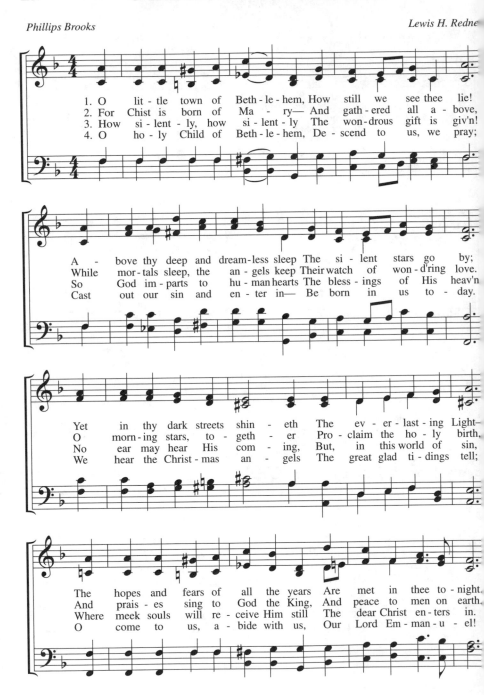

1. O lit - tle town of Beth - le - hem, How still we see thee lie!
2. For Chist is born of Ma - ry— And gath - ered all a - bove,
3. How si - lent - ly, how si - lent - ly The won - drous gift is giv'n!
4. O ho - ly Child of Beth - le - hem, De - scend to us, we pray;

A - bove thy deep and dream-less sleep The si - lent stars go by;
While mor - tals sleep, the an - gels keep Their watch of won - d'ring love.
So God im - parts to hu - man hearts The bless - ings of His heav'n
Cast out our sin and en - ter in— Be born in us to - day.

Yet in thy dark streets shin - eth The ev - er - last - ing Light—
O morn - ing stars, to - geth - er Pro - claim the ho - ly birth,
No ear may hear His com - ing, But, in this world of sin,
We hear the Christ - mas an - gels The great glad ti - dings tell;

The hopes and fears of all the years Are met in thee to - night.
And prais - es sing to God the King, And peace to men on earth.
Where meek souls will re - ceive Him still The dear Christ en - ters in.
O come to us, a - bide with us, Our Lord Em - man - u - el!

Silent Night! Holy Night!

Joseph Mohr

Franz Gruber

1. Si - lent night! ho - ly night! All is calm,
2. Si - lent night! ho - ly night! Shep - herds quake
3. Si - lent night! ho - ly night! Son of God,
4. Si - lent night! ho - ly night! Won - drous Star,

all is bright, Round yon Vir - gin Moth - er and Child!
at the sight, Glo - ries stream from heav - en a - far,
love's pure Light Ra - diant beams from Thy ho - ly face,
lend thy light; With the an - gels let us sing,

Ho - ly In - fant, so ten - der and mild, Sleep in
Heaven - ly hosts sing: "Al - le - lu - ia; Christ the
With the dawn of re - deem - ing grace, Je - sus,
Al - le - lu - ia to our King; Christ the

heav - en - ly peace, Sleep in heav - en - ly peace.
Sav - iour is born, Christ the Sav - iour is born."
Lord, at Thy birth, Je - sus, Lord, at Thy birth.
Sav - iour is born, Christ the Sav - iour is born.

31

One Day!

J. Wilbur Chapman

Charles H. Mars

1. One day when heav - en was filled with His prais - es, One day when
2. One day they led Him up Cal - va - ry's moun - tain, One day they
3. One day they left Him a - lone in the gar - den, One day He
4. One day the grave could con - ceal Him no long - er, One day the
5. One day the trump - et will sound for His com - ing, One day the

sin was as black as could be, Je - sus came forth to be
nailed Him to die on the tree; Suf - fer - ing an - guish, de
rest - ed, from suf - fer - ing free; An - gels came down o'er Hi
stone rolled a - way from the door; Then He a - rose, o - ve
skies with His glo - ry will shine; Won - der - ful day; my be

born of a vir - gin— Dwelt a - mong men, my ex - am - ple is He!
spised and re - ject - ed: Bear - ing our sins, my Re - deem - er is He!
tomb to keep vig - il; Hope of the hope - less, my Sav - ior is He!
death He had con - quered; Now is as - cend - ed, My Lord ev - er - more!
lov - ed ones bring - ing; Glo - ri - ous Sav - ior, this Je - sus is mine!

Chorus

Liv - ing, He loved me; dy - ing, He saved me; Bur - ied, He

car - ried my sins far a - way; Ris - ing, He jus - ti - fied

free - ly for - ev - er: One day He's com - ing— oh, glo - ri - ous day!

Tell Me the Stories of Jesus 32

William H. Parker

Frederic A. Challinor

1. Tell me the sto-ries of Je - sus I love to hear; Things I would
2. First let me hear how the chil-dren Stood round His knee, And I shall
3. In - to the cit - y I'd fol - low The chil - dren's band, Wav-ing a

ask Him to tell me If He were here: Scenes by the way - side,
fan - cy His bless - ing Rest-ing on me; Words full of kind - ness,
branch of the palm-tree High in my hand; One of His her - alds,

Tales of the sea, Sto - ries of Je - sus, Tell them to me.
Deeds full of grace, All in the love - light Of Je - sus' face.
Yes, I would sing Loud-est ho - san - nas, "Je - sus is King!"

33 At Calvary

William R. Newell

Daniel B. Towner

1. Years I spent in van - i - ty and pride, Car - ing
2. By God's Word at last my sin I learned; Then I
3. Now I've given to Je - sus ev - ery - thing; Now I
4. Oh, the love that drew sal - va - tion's plan! Oh, the

not my Lord was cru - ci - fied, Know - ing not it was for
trem - bled at the law I'd spurned Till my guilt - y soul im
glad - ly own Him as my King; Now my rap - tured soul can
grace that brought it down to man! Oh, the might - y gulf that

me He died On Cal - va - ry.
plor - ing turned To Cal - va - ry.
on - ly sing Of Cal - va - ry.
God did span At Cal - va - ry!

Refrain

Mer - cy there was great, an

grace was free; Par - don there was mul - ti - plied to me;

There my bur - dened soul found lib - er - ty— At Cal - va - ry.

At the Cross

34

Isaac Watts
Refrain: Ralph E. Hudson

Ralph E. Hudson

1. A - las, and did my Sav - iour bleed? And did my Sov - 'reign die?
2. Was it for crimes that I have done, He groaned up - on the tree?
3. Well might the sun in dark - ness hide, And shut his glo - ries in,
4. But drops of grief can ne'er re - pay The debt of love I owe:

Would He de - vote that sa - cred head For such a worm as I?
A - maz - ing pit - y! grace un - known! And love be - yond de - gree!
When Christ, the might - y Mak - er, died For man the crea - ture's sin.
Here, Lord, I give my - self a - way, 'Tis all that I can do!

Refrain

At the cross, at the cross where I first saw the light, And the

bur - den of my heart rolled a - way, (rolled a - way,) It was there by faith

I re - ceived my sight, And now I am hap - py all the day!

35 Beneath the Cross of Jesus

Elizabeth C. Clephane

Frederick C. Maker

1. Be - neath the cross of Je - sus I fain would take my stand, The
2. Up - on that cross of Je - sus Mine eye at times can see The
3. I take, O cross, thy shad - ow For my a - bid - ing place; I

shad - ow of a might - y rock With - in a wea - ry land; A
ver - y dy - ing form of One Who suf - fered there for me; And
ask no oth - er sun - shine than The sun - shine of His face; Con -

home with - in the wil - der - ness, A rest up - on the way, From the
from my smit - ten heart with tears Two won - ders I con - fess— The
tent to let the world go by, To know no gain nor loss. My

burn - ing of the noon - tide heat, And the bur - den of the day.
won - ders of re - deem - ing love, And my un - wor - thi - ness.
sin - ful self my on - ly shame, My glo - ry all the cross.

Hallelujah, What a Savior!

Philip P. Bliss   *Philip P. Bliss*

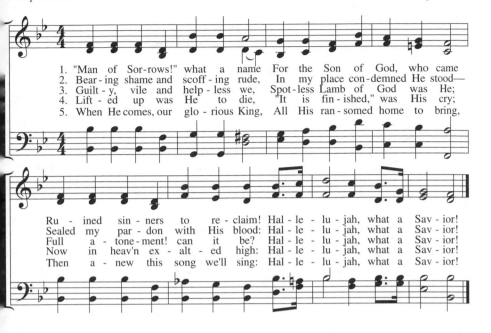

1. "Man of Sor-rows!" what a name For the Son of God, who came
2. Bear-ing shame and scoff-ing rude, In my place con-demned He stood—
3. Guilt-y, vile and help-less we, Spot-less Lamb of God was He;
4. Lift-ed up was He to die, "It is fin-ished," was His cry;
5. When He comes, our glo-rious King, All His ran-somed home to bring,

Ru - ined sin - ners to re - claim! Hal - le - lu - jah, what a Sav - ior!
Sealed my par - don with His blood: Hal - le - lu - jah, what a Sav - ior!
Full a - tone - ment! can it be? Hal - le - lu - jah, what a Sav - ior!
Now in heav'n ex - alt - ed high: Hal - le - lu - jah, what a Sav - ior!
Then a - new this song we'll sing: Hal - le - lu - jah, what a Sav - ior!

When I Survey the Wondrous Cross   37

Isaac Watts   *Lowell Mason*

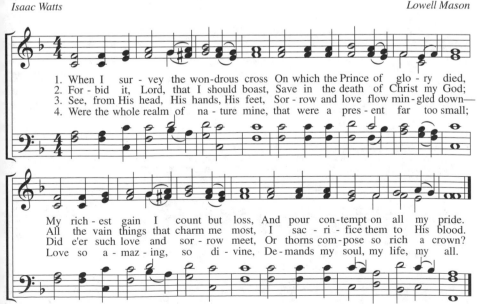

1. When I sur - vey the won-drous cross On which the Prince of glo - ry died,
2. For - bid it, Lord, that I should boast, Save in the death of Christ my God;
3. See, from His head, His hands, His feet, Sor - row and love flow min-gled down—
4. Were the whole realm of na - ture mine, that were a pres - ent far too small;

My rich - est gain I count but loss, And pour con-tempt on all my pride.
All the vain things that charm me most, I sac - ri - fice them to His blood.
Did e'er such love and sor - row meet, Or thorns com-pose so rich a crown?
Love so a - maz - ing, so di - vine, De-mands my soul, my life, my all.

38   The Old Rugged Cross

George Bennard   *George Bennard*

1. On a hill far a-way stood an old rug-ged cross, The em-blem of
2. Oh, that old rug-ged cross, so de-spised by the world, Has a won-drous a
3. In the old rug-ged cross, stained with blood so di-vine, A won-drou
4. To the old rug-ged cross I will ev-er be true, Its shame and re

suf-fering and shame; And I love that old cross where the dear-est and best
trac-tion for me; For the dear Lamb of God left His glo-ry a-bove
beau-ty I see; For 'twas on that old cross Je-sus suf-fered and died
proach glad-ly bear; Then He'll call me some day to my home far a-way

Chorus

For a world of lost sin-ners was slain.
To bear it to dark Cal-va-ry. So I'll cher-ish the old rug-ged
To par-don and sanc-ti-fy me. cross, the
Where His glo-ry for-ev-er I'll share.

cross, Till my tro-phies at last I lay down; I will cling to the
old rug-ged cross,

old rug-ged cross And ex-change it some day for a crown.
cross, the old rug-ged cross,

Because He Lives

Gloria & William J. Gaither

William J. Gaither

1. God sent His Son, they called Him Je - sus; He came to love, heal,
2. How sweet to hold a new-born ba - by, And feel the pride and
3. And then one day I'll cross the riv - er; I'll fight life's fi - nal

and for - give; He lived and died to buy my par - don, An emp - ty
joy he gives; But great - er still the calm as - sur - ance, This child can
war with pain; And then as death gives way to vic - t'ry, I'll see the

Refrain

grave is there to prove my Sav - ior lives.
face un - cer - tain days be - cause He lives. Be-cause He lives I can face to-
lights of glo - ry and I'll know He lives.

mor - row; Be-cause He lives all fear is gone; Be-cause I know He

holds the fu - ture, And life is worth the liv - ing just be-cause He lives.

40   He Lives

Alfred H. Ackley   *Alfred H. Ackley*

1. I serve a ris-en Sav-ior, He's in the world to-day; I know that He is
2. In all the world a-round me I see His lov-ing care, And tho' my heart grow
3. Re-joice, re-joice, O Chris-tian, lift up your voice and sing E-ter-nal hal-le-

liv-ing, what-ev-er men may say; I see His hand of mer-cy, I
wea-ry, I nev-er will de-spair; I know that He is lead-ing thro'
lu-jahs to Je-sus Christ the King! The Hope of all who seek Him, the

hear His voice of cheer, And just the time I need Him He's al-ways near.
all the storm-y blast, The day of His ap-pear-ing will come at last.
Help of all who find, None oth-er is so lov-ing, so good and kind.

Refrain

He lives, He lives, Christ Je-sus lives to-day! He walks with me and
He lives, He lives,

talks with me a-long life's nar-row way. He lives, He lives, sal-
He lives, He lives,

va-tion to im - part! You ask me how I know He lives? He lives with-in my heart.

Jesus Shall Reign

41

Isaac Watts

John Hatton

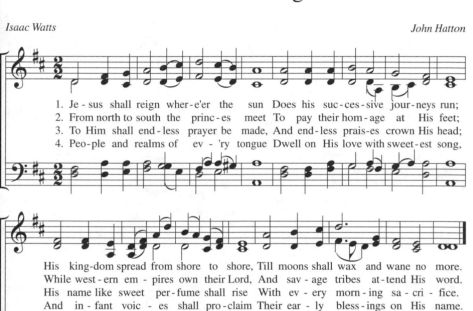

1. Je - sus shall reign wher-e'er the sun Does his suc-ces-sive jour-neys run;
2. From north to south the princ-es meet To pay their hom-age at His feet;
3. To Him shall end-less prayer be made, And end-less prais-es crown His head;
4. Peo-ple and realms of ev - 'ry tongue Dwell on His love with sweet-est song,

His king-dom spread from shore to shore, Till moons shall wax and wane no more.
While west-ern em - pires own their Lord, And sav-age tribes at-tend His word.
His name like sweet per-fume shall rise With ev-ery morn-ing sa-cri-fice.
And in-fant voic-es shall pro-claim Their ear - ly bless-ings on His name.

42 Christ Arose

Robert Lowry

Robert Lowry

1. Low in the grave He lay— Je - sus, my Sav-ior! Wait-ing the com-ing day—
2. Vain - ly they watch His bed— Je - sus, my Sav-ior! Vain - ly they seal the dead—
3. Death can - not keep his prey— Je - sus, my Sav-ior! He tore the bars a - way—

Chorus Faster

Je - sus, my Lord!
Je - sus, my Lord! Up from the grave He a - rose, With a
Je - sus, my Lord!

He a - rose,

might - y tri - umph o'er His foes; He a - rose a Vic - tor from the

He a - rose!

dark do - main, And He lives for - ev - er with His saints to reign: He a-

rose! He a - rose! Hal - le - lu - jah! Christ a - rose!

He a-rose! He a - rose!

Christ the Lord Is Risen Today! 43

Charles Wesley

From Lyra Davidica

1. Christ the Lord is risen to-day, Al - - - le - lu - ia!
2. Lives a-gain our glo-rious King, Al - - - le - lu - ia!
3. Love's re-deem-ing work is done, Al - - - le - lu - ia!
4. Soar we now where Christ has led, Al - - - le - lu - ia!

Sons of men and an-gels say, Al - - - le - lu - ia!
Where, O death, is now thy sting? Al - - - le - lu - ia!
Fought the fight, the bat-tle won, Al - - - le - lu - ia!
Fol-lowing our ex-alt-ed Head, Al - - - le - lu - ia!

Raise your joys and tri-umphs high, Al - - - le - lu - ia!
Once He died, our souls to save, Al - - - le - lu - ia!
Death in vain for-bids Him rise, Al - - - le - lu - ia!
Made like Him, like Him we rise, Al - - - le - lu - ia!

Sing, ye heavens, and earth re-ply, Al - - - le - lu - ia!
Where's thy vic-tory, boast-ing grave? Al - - - le - lu - ia!
Christ hath o-pened Par-a-dise, Al - - - le - lu - ia!
Ours the cross, the grave, the skies, Al - - - le - lu - ia!

44   What If It Were Today?

Lelia N. Morris   *Lelia N. Morris*

1. Je - sus is com - ing to earth a - gain— What if it were to - day?
2. Sat - an's do - min - ion will then be o'er— O that it were to - day!
3. Faith - ful and true would He find us here If He should come to - day?

Com - ing in pow - er and love to reign— What if it were to - day?
Sor - row and sigh - ing shall be no more— O that it were to - day!
Watch - ing in glad - ness and not in fear, If He should come to - day?

Com - ing to claim His cho - sen Bride, All the re - deemed and pu - ri - fied,
Then shall the dead in Christ a - rise, Caught up to meet Him in the skies;
Signs of His com - ing mul - ti - ply, Morn - ing light breaks in east - ern sky;

rit.   *a tempo*

O - ver this whole earth scat - tered wide— What if it were to - day?
When shall these glo - ries meet our eyes? What if it were to - day?
Watch, for the time is draw - ing nigh— What if it were to - day?

Chorus

Glo - ry, glo - ry! Joy to my heart 'twill bring, Glo - ry, glo - ry!

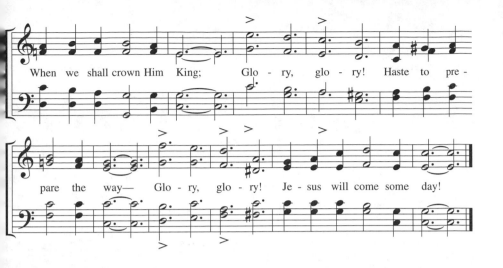

When we shall crown Him King; Glo - ry, glo - ry! Haste to pre -
pare the way— Glo - ry, glo - ry! Je - sus will come some day!

Break Thou the Bread of Life   45

Mary Ann Lathbury   *William F. Sherwin*

1. Break Thou the bread of life, Dear Lord, to me, As Thou didst
2. Bless Thou the truth, dear Lord, To me— to me, As Thou didst
3. Thou art the bread of life, O Lord, to me; Thy ho - ly
4. O send Thy Spir - it, Lord, Now un - to me, That He may

break the loaves Be - side the sea: Be - yond the sa - cred page
bless the bread By Gal - i - lee: Then shall all bond - age cease,
Word the truth That sav - eth me: Give me to eat and live
touch my eyes And make me see: Show me the truth con - cealed

I seek Thee, Lord; My spir - it pants for Thee, O liv - ing Word.
All fet - ters fall, And I shall find my peace, My All in all.
With Thee a - bove; Teach me to love Thy truth, For Thou art love.
With - in Thy Word, And in Thy book re - vealed I see Thee, Lord.

46

The Bible Stands

Haldor Lillenas   *Haldor Lillenas*

1. The Bi - ble stands like a rock un - daunt - ed 'Mid the rag - ing
2. The Bi - ble stands like a moun - tain tow - 'ring Far a - bove the
3. The Bi - ble stands, and it will for - ev - er When the world has
4. The Bi - ble stands ev - 'ry test we give it For its Au - thor

storms of time; Its pag - es burn with the truth e - ter - nal, And they
works of men; Its truth by none ev - er was re - fut - ed, And de -
passed a - way; By in - spi - ra - tion it has been gi - ven All its
is di - vine; By grace a - lone I ex - pect to live it And to

Chorus

glow with a light sub - lime.
stroy it they nev - er can.
pre - cepts I will o - bey.   The Bi - ble stands tho the hills may
prove it and make it mine.

tum - ble, It will firm - ly stand when the earth shall crum - ble; I will

plant my feet on its firm foun - da - tion For the Bi - ble stands.

Wonderful Words of Life

Philip P. Bliss   *Philip P. Bliss*

1. Sing them o - ver a - gain to me, Won - der - ful words of Life;
2. Christ, the bless - ed One, gives to all, Won - der - ful words of Life;
3. Sweet - ly ech - o the gos - pel call, Won - der - ful words of Life;

Let me more of their beau - ty see, Won - der - ful words of Life.
Sin - ner, list to the lov - ing call, Won - der - ful words of Life.
Of - fer par - don and peace to all, Won - der - ful words of Life.

Words of life and beau - ty, Teach me faith and du - ty:
All so free - ly giv - en, Woo - ing us to Heav - en:
Je - sus, on - ly Sav - iour, Sanc - ti - fy for - ev - er:

Refrain

Beau - ti - ful words, won - der - ful words, Won - der - ful words of Life. Life.

48 Glorious Things of Thee Are Spoken

John Newton   *Franz Joseph Haydn*

1. Glo - rious things of thee are spo - ken, Zi - on, cit - y
2. See, the streams of liv - ing wa - ters, Spring - ing from e -
3. Round each hab - i - ta - tion hov - 'ring, See the cloud and
4. Blest in - hab - i - tants of Zi - on, Washed in the Re -
5. Sav - iour, if of Zi - on's cit - y I, through grace, a

of our God; He whose word can - not be bro - ken
ter - nal love, Well sup - ply thy sons and daugh - ters,
fire ap - pear For a glo - ry and a cov - 'ring,
deem - er's blood; Je - sus, whom their souls re - ly on,
mem - ber am, Let the world de - ride or pi - ty—

Formed thee for His own a - bode: On the Rock of A -
And all fear of want re - move: Who can faint, when such
Show - ing that the Lord is near; Thus de - riv - ing from
Makes them kings and priests to God. 'Tis His love His peo -
I will glo - ry in Thy name. Fad - ing is the world -

ges found - ed, What can shake thy sure re - pose? With sal -
a riv - er Ev - er flows their thirst t'as - suage; Grace, which,
their ban - ner Light by night, and shade by day, Safe they
ple rais - es O - ver self to reign as kings; And as
ling's pleas - ure, All his boast - ed pomp and show; Sol - id

va - tion's walls sur - round - ed, Thou may'st smile at all thy foes.
like the Lord, the giv - er, Nev - er fails from age to age.
feed up - on the man - na Which He gives them when they pray.
priests, His sol - emn prais - es, Each for a thank of - fering brings.
joys and last - ing treas - ure None but Zi - on's chil - dren know.

Blest Be the Tie That Binds   49

John Fawcett   *Johann H. G. Nageli*

1. Blest be the tie that binds Our hearts in Chris - tian love; The
2. Be - fore our Fa - ther's throne We pour our ar - dent prayers; Our
3. We share our mu - tual woes, Our mu - tual bur - dens bear; And
4. When we a - sun - der part It gives us in - ward pain; But

fel - low - ship of kin - dred minds Is like to that a - bove.
fears, our hopes, our aims are one, Our com - forts and our cares.
oft - en for each oth - er flows The sym - pa - thiz - ing tear.
we shall still be joined in heart And hope to meet a - gain.

50 The Church's One Foundation

Samuel J. Stone

Samuel S. Wesley

1. The Chur-ch's one Foun-da-tion Is Je-sus Christ her Lord;
2. E-lect from ev-ery na-tion Yet one o'er all the earth,
3. Though with a scorn-ful won-der Men see her sore op-pressed,
4. 'Mid toil and trib-u-la-tion And tu-mult of her war,
5. Yet she on earth hath un-ion With God the Three in One,

She is His new cre-a-tion By wa-ter and the word:
Her char-ter of sal-va-tion, One Lord, one faith, one birth;
By schisms rent a-sun-der, By her-e-sies dis-tressed,
She waits the con-sum-ma-tion Of peace for-ev-er-more;
And mys-tic sweet com-mun-ion With those whose rest is won.

From heaven He came and sought her To be His ho-ly bride;
One ho-ly name she bless-es, Par-takes one ho-ly food,
Yet saints their watch are keep-ing; Their cry goes up— "How long?"
Till with the vi-sion glo-rious Her long-ing eyes are blest,
Oh, hap-py ones and ho-ly! Lord, give us grace that we,

With His own blood He bought her, And for her life He died.
And to one hope she press-es, With ev-ery grace en-dued,
But soon the night of weep-ing Shall be the morn of song.
And the great Church vic-to-rious Shall be the Church at rest.
Like them, the meek and low-ly, On high may dwell with Thee.

We Gather Together

51

Anon.
Trans. by Theodore Baker

Netherlands Folksong
Arr. by Edward Kremser

1. We gath - er to - geth - er to ask the Lord's bless - ing;
2. Be - side us to guide us, our God with us join - ing,
3. We all do ex - tol Thee, Thou Lead - er tri - um - phant,

He chas - tens and has - tens His will to make known;
Or - dain - ing, main - tain - ing His king - dom di - vine;
And pray that Thou still our De - fend - er wilt be.

The wick - ed op - press - ing now cease from dis - tress - ing,
So from the be - gin - ning the fight we were win - ning:
Let Thy con - gre - ga - tion es - cape trib - u - la - tion:

Sing prais - es to His Name: He for - gets not His own.
Thou, Lord, wast at our side, all - glo - ry be Thine!
Thy Name be ev - er praised! O Lord, make us free!

Onward, Christian Soldiers

Sabine Baring-Gould   *Arthur S. Sulliva*

1. On - ward, Chris - tian sol - diers, March - ing as to war,
2. Like a might - y ar - my Moves the Church of God;
3. Crowns and thrones may per - ish, King - doms rise and wane,
4. On - ward, then, ye peo - ple, Join our hap - py throng,

With the cross of Je - sus Go - ing on be - fore: Christ, the roy - al
Broth - ers, we are tread - ing Where the saints have trod; We are not di
But the Church of Je - sus Con - stant will re - main; Gates of hell ca
Blend with ours your voic - es In the tri - umph song; Glo - ry, laud, an

Mas - ter, Leads a - gainst the foe; For - ward in - to bat - tle,
vid - ed, All one bod - y we, One in hope and doc - trine,
nev - er 'Gainst that Church pre - vail; We have Christ's own prom - ise,
hon - or Un - to Christ the King; This through count - less a - ges

See, His ban - ners go.
One in char - i - ty.
And that can - not fail.
Men and an - gels sing.

Refrain

On-ward, Chris-tian sol - diers, March-ing as to

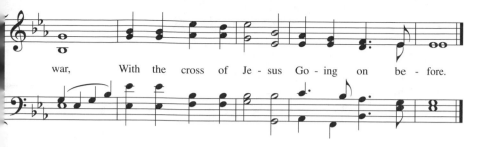

war, With the cross of Je - sus Go - ing on be - fore.

Cleanse Me

53

Edwin Orr

Maori Melody by John McNeill
Arr. by Norman Johnson

1. Search me, O God, and know my heart to - day; Try me, O
2. I praise Thee, Lord, for cleans-ing me from sin: Ful - fill Thy
3. Lord, take my life, and make it whol - ly Thine: Fill my poor
4. O Ho - ly Ghost, re - viv - al comes from Thee: Send a re -

Sav - ior, know my thoughts, I pray: See if there be some wick - ed
Word, and make me pure with - in; Fill me with fire, where once I
heart with Thy great love di - vine; Take all my will, my pas - sion,
viv - al— start the work in me: Thy Word de - clares Thou wilt sup-

way in me: Cleanse me from ev - 'ry sin, and set me free.
burned with shame: Grant my de - sire to mag - ni - fy Thy name.
self and pride; I now sur - ren - der: Lord, in me a - bide.
ply our need: For bless - ing now, O Lord, I hum - bly plead.

54   I Surrender All

Judson W. Van DeVenter   *Winfield S. Weede*

1. All to Je - sus I sur-ren - der, All to Him I free - ly give;
2. All to Je - sus I sur-ren - der, Make me, Sav - ior, whol - ly Thine;
3. All to Je - sus I sur-ren - der, Lord, I give my - self to Thee;

I will ev - er love and trust Him, In His pres - ence dai - ly live.
Let me feel the Ho - ly Spir - it— Tru - ly know that Thou art mine.
Fill me with Thy love and pow - er, Let Thy bless - ing fall on me.

Refrain

I sur-ren - der all, I sur-ren - der all;
I sur-ren-der all, I sur-ren-der all;

All to Thee, my bless - ed Sav - ior, I sur-ren - der all.

Jesus Is Calling

Fanny J. Crosby

George C. Stebbins

1. Je - sus is ten - der - ly call - ing thee home— Call - ing to - day,
2. Je - sus is call - ing the wea - ry to rest— Call - ing to - day,
3. Je - sus is wait - ing, O come to Him now— Wait - ing to - day,
4. Je - sus is plead - ing, O list to His voice— Hear Him to - day,

call - ing to - day; Why from the sun - shine of love wilt thou roam
call - ing to - day; Bring Him thy bur - den and thou shalt be blest—
wait - ing to - day; Come with thy sins, at His feet low - ly bow—
hear Him to - day; They who be - lieve on His name shall re - joice—

Refrain

Far - ther and far - ther a - way?
He will not turn thee a - way.
Come, and no long - er de - lay.   Call - ing to - day,
Quick - ly a - rise and a - way.   Call - ing, call - ing to - day, to - day,

Call - ing to - day,   Je - sus is
Call - ing, call - ing to - day, to - day;   Je - sus is ten - der - ly

call - ing Is ten - der - ly call - ing to - day.
call - ing to - day,

Lord, I'm Coming Home

William J. Kirkpatrick

William J. Kirkpatri

1. I've wan-dered far a - way from God— Now I'm com-ing home; The paths o
2. I've wast-ed man-y pre - cious years—Now I'm com-ing home; I   now r
3. I've tired of sin and stray - ing, Lord—Now I'm com-ing home; I'll trust Th
4. My soul is sick, my heart is sore— Now I'm com-ing home; My strength r

Chorus

sin   too long I've trod—Lord, I'm com-ing home.
pent with bit - ter tears—Lord, I'm com-ing home.
love, be - lieve Thy Word—Lord, I'm com-ing home.   Com-ing home, com-ing hon
new, my hope re - store—Lord, I'm com-ing home.

Nev-er-more to   roam;   O-pen now Thine arms of love—Lord, I'm com-ing home.

Only Trust Him

John H. Stockton

John H. Stock

1. Come, ev - 'ry soul by sin op-pressed—There's mer - cy with the Lo
2. For   Je - sus shed His pre - cious blood Rich bless-ings to be - sto
3. Yes,   Je - sus is the Truth, the Way, That leads you in - to res

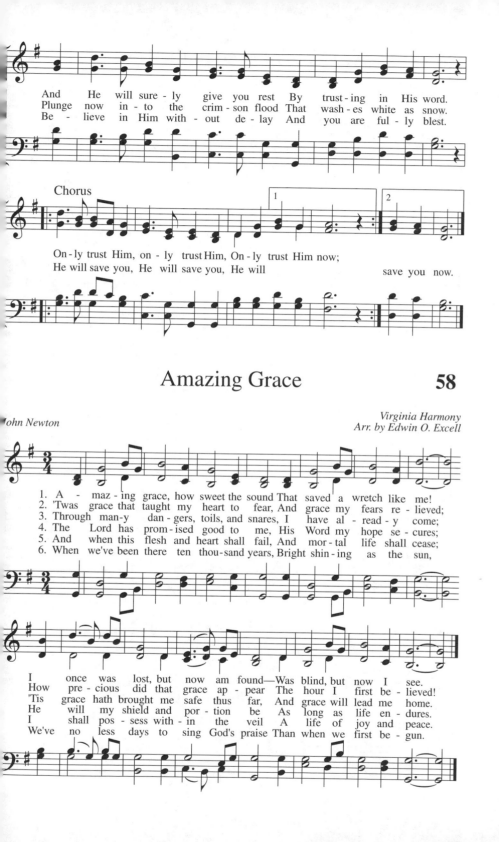

Amazing Grace 58

59   Are You Washed in the Blood?

Elisha A. Hoffman   Elisha A. Hoffman

Blessed Assurance

Fanny J. Crosby

Mrs. Joseph F. Knapp

1. Bless-ed as - sur - ance, Je - sus is mine! O what a fore - taste of
2. Per - fect sub - mis - sion, per - fect de - light, Vi - sions of rap - ture now
3. Per - fect sub - mis - sion, all is at rest, I in my Sav - ior am

glo - ry di - vine! Heir of sal - va - tion, pur - chase of God, Born of His
burst on my sight; An - gels de - scend - ing, bring from a - bove, Ech - oes of
hap - py and blest, Watch-ing and wait - ing, look - ing a - bove, Filled with His

Refrain

Spir - it, washed in His blood. This is my sto - ry, this is my
mer - cy, whis - pers of love.
good - ness, lost in His love.

song, Prais - ing my Sav - ior all the day long; This is my

sto - ry, this is my song: Prais-ing my Sav - ior all the day long.

61   # Glory to His Name

Elisha A. Hoffman   *John H. Stockton*

1. Down at the cross where my Sav - ior died, Down where for cleans - ing from
2. I am so won-drous-ly saved from sin; Je - sus so sweet - ly a
3. Oh, pre-cious foun-tain that saves from sin! I am so glad I hav
4. Come to this foun-tain so rich and sweet; Cast thy poor soul at the

sin I cried—There to my heart was the blood ap - plied; Glo-ry to His name
bides with - in, There at the cross where He took me in; Glo-ry to His name
en - tered in; There Je - sus saves me and keeps me clean; Glo-ry to His name
Sav - ior's feet; Plunge in to - day and be made com-plete; Glo-ry to His name

Refrain

Glo - ry to His name, Glo - ry to His name;

There to my heart was the blood ap - plied; Glo - ry to His name!

Grace Greater Than Our Sin

62

Julia H. Johnston

Daniel B. Towner

1. Mar - vel - ous grace of our lov - ing Lord, Grace that ex - ceeds our
2. Sin and de - spair like the sea waves cold, Threat - en the soul with
3. Dark is the stain that we can - not hide, What can a - vail to
4. Mar - vel - ous, in - fi - nite, match - less grace, Free - ly be - stowed on

sin and our guilt, Yon - der on Cal - va - ry's mount out - poured,
in - fi - nite loss; Grace that is great - er, yes, grace un - told,
wash it a - way? Look! there is flow - ing a crim - son tide;
all who be - lieve; You that are long - ing to see His face,

Refrain

There where the blood of the Lamb was spilt. Grace, grace,
Points to the Ref - uge, the might - y Cross. Mar - vel - ous grace,
Whit - er than snow you may be to - day.
Will you this mo - ment His grace re - ceive?

God's grace, Grace that will par - don and cleanse with - in; Grace,
in - fi - nite grace, Mar - vel - ous

grace, God's grace, Grace that is great - er than all our sin.
grace, in - fi - nite grace,

63   He Is Able to Deliver Thee

William A. Ogden   *William A. Ogde*

1. 'Tis the grand-est theme thru the a - ges rung, 'Tis the grand-est theme for a
2. 'Tis the grand-est theme in the earth or main, 'Tis the grand-est theme for a
3. 'Tis the grand-est theme, let the ti - dings roll, To the guilt - y heart, to th

mor-tal tongue; 'Tis the grand-est theme that the world e'er sung— "Our God is
mor-tal strain; 'Tis the grand-est theme, tell the world a - gain— "Our God is
sin - ful soul; Look to God in faith, He will make thee whole— "Our God is

Chorus

a - ble to de - liv - er thee." He is a - - - ble to de - liv - er thee.
                       He is a-ble, He is a-ble

He is a - - - ble to de - liv - er thee; Tho by sin op - pres
He is a-ble, He is a-ble

Go to Him for rest: "Our God is a - ble to de - liv - er thee."

He Lifted Me

Charles H. Gabriel

Charles H. Gabriel

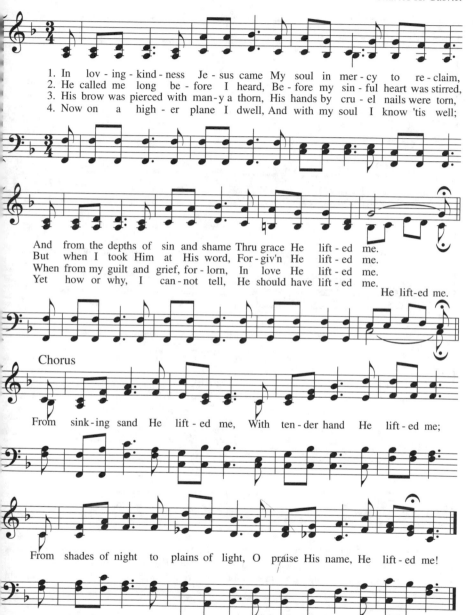

1. In lov - ing - kind - ness Je - sus came My soul in mer - cy to re - claim,
2. He called me long be - fore I heard, Be - fore my sin - ful heart was stirred,
3. His brow was pierced with man - y a thorn, His hands by cru - el nails were torn,
4. Now on a high - er plane I dwell, And with my soul I know 'tis well;

And from the depths of sin and shame Thru grace He lift - ed me.
But when I took Him at His word, For - giv'n He lift - ed me.
When from my guilt and grief, for - lorn, In love He lift - ed me.
Yet how or why, I can - not tell, He should have lift - ed me.

He lift-ed me.

Chorus

From sink - ing sand He lift - ed me, With ten - der hand He lift - ed me;

From shades of night to plains of light, O praise His name, He lift - ed me!

65

Heaven Came Down and Glory Filled My Soul

John W. Peterson   *John W. Peters*

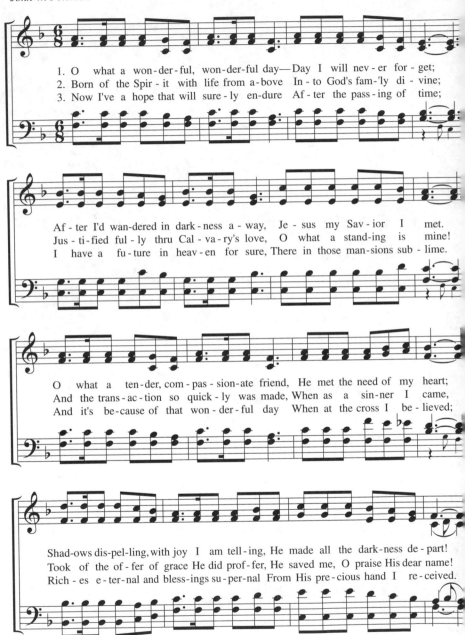

1. O what a won-der-ful, won-der-ful day—Day I will nev-er for-get;
2. Born of the Spir-it with life from a-bove In-to God's fam-'ly di-vine;
3. Now I've a hope that will sure-ly en-dure Af-ter the pass-ing of time;

Af-ter I'd wan-dered in dark-ness a-way, Je-sus my Sav-ior I met.
Jus-ti-fied ful-ly thru Cal-va-ry's love, O what a stand-ing is mine!
I have a fu-ture in heav-en for sure, There in those man-sions sub-lime.

O what a ten-der, com-pas-sion-ate friend, He met the need of my heart;
And the trans-ac-tion so quick-ly was made, When as a sin-ner I came,
And it's be-cause of that won-der-ful day When at the cross I be-lieved;

Shad-ows dis-pel-ling, with joy I am tell-ing, He made all the dark-ness de-part!
Took of the of-fer of grace He did prof-fer, He saved me, O praise His dear name!
Rich-es e-ter-nal and bless-ings su-per-nal From His pre-cious hand I re-ceived.

Chorus

Heav - en came down and glo - ry filled my soul,

filled my soul,

When at the cross the Sav - ior made me whole;

made me whole;

My sins were washed a - way And my night was turned to day—

Heav - en came down and glo - ry filled my soul!

filled my soul!

66   I Know Whom I Have Believed

Daniel W. Whittle

James McGranah

1. I know not why God's won-drous grace To me He hath made known
2. I know not how this sav - ing faith To me He did im - part,
3. I know not how the Spir - it moves, Con - vinc-ing men of sin,
4. I know not when my Lord may come, At night or noon-day fair,

Nor why Christ, in His bound - less love, Re-deemed me for His own.
Nor how be - liev-ing in His Word Wrought peace with-in my heart
Re - veal - ing Je - sus through the Word, Cre - at - ing faith in Him
Nor if I'll walk the vale with Him, Or "meet Him in the air."

Refrain

But "I know whom I have be - liev - ed, and am per - suad - ed that He

a - ble To keep that which I've com - mit - ted Un - to Him a-gainst that day

I Will Praise Him

Margaret J. Harris   *Margaret J. Harris*

1. When I saw the cleans-ing foun-tain O - pen wide for all my sin,
2. Tho' the way seems straight and nar-row, All I claimed was swept a - way;
3. Then God's fire up - on the al - tar Of my heart was set a - flame;
4. Bless - ed be the name of Je - sus! I'm so glad He took me in;
5. Glo - ry, glo - ry to the Fa - ther! Glo - ry, glo - ry to the Son!

I o - beyed the Spir - it's woo - ing, When He said, Wilt thou be clean?
My am - bi - tions, plans, and wish - es, At my feet in ash - es lay.
I shall nev - er cease to praise Him, Glo - ry, glo - ry to His name!
He's for - giv - en my trans - gres - sions, He has cleansed my heart from sin.
Glo - ry, glo - ry to the Spir - it! Glo - ry to the Three in One!

Chorus *Faster*

I will praise Him! I will praise Him! Praise the Lamb for sin-ners slain;

for sin-ners slain;

Give Him glo-ry, all ye peo-ple, For His blood can wash a-way each stain.

68   I Will Sing the Wondrous Story

Francis H. Rowley

Peter P. Bilhorn

1. I will sing the won-drous sto-ry Of the Christ who died for me,
2. I was lost, but Je-sus found me, Found the sheep that went a-stray,
3. I was bruised, but Jesus healed me; Faint was I from man-y a fall;
4. Days of dark-ness still come o'er me, Sor-row's paths I oft-en tread,
5. He will keep me till the riv-er Rolls its wa-ters at my feet;

How He left His home in glo-ry For the cross of Cal-va-ry.
Threw His lov-ing arms a-round me, Drew me back in-to His way.
Sight was gone, and fears pos-sessed me, But He freed me from them all.
But the Sav-iour still is with me; By His hand I'm safe-ly led.
Then He'll bear me safe-ly o-ver Where the loved ones I shall meet.

Refrain

Yes, I'll sing the won-drous sto-ry Of the
Yes, I'll sing the won-drous sto-ry, won-drous sto-ry

Christ who died for me, Sing it with the saints in
Of the Christ Sing it with the saints in

glo-ry Gath-ered by the crys-tal sea.
glo-ry, saints in glo-ry Gath-ered by

The Light of the World

Philip P. Bliss   *Philip P. Bliss*

1. The whole world was lost in the dark-ness of sin; The Light of the
2. No dark-ness have we who in Je-sus a-bide, The Light of the
3. Ye dwell-ers in dark-ness with sin-blind-ed eyes, The Light of the
4. No need of the sun-light in heav-en we're told, The Light of the

world is Je-sus; Like sun-shine at noon-day His glo-ry shone in,
world is Je-sus; We walk in the light when we fol-low our guide,
world is Je-sus; Go, wash at His bid-ding, and light will a-rise,
world is Je-sus; The Lamb is the Light in the cit-y of gold,

Refrain

The Light of the world is Je-sus. Come to the Light, 'tis

shin-ing for thee; Sweet-ly the Light has dawned up-on me;

Once I was blind, but now I can see; The Light of the world is Je-sus.

70   Let Jesus Come into Your Heart

Leila N. Morris   *Leila N. Morris*

1. If you are tired of the load of your sin, Let Jesus come in-to your heart; If you de-sire a new life to be-gin, Let Jesus come into your heart.

2. If 'tis for pu-ri-ty now that you sigh, Let Jesus come in-to your heart; Foun-tains for cleans-ing are flow-ing near by, Let Jesus come into your heart.

3. If there's a tem-pest your voice can-not still, Let Jesus come in-to your heart; If there's a void this world nev-er can fill, Let Jesus come into your heart.

4. If you would join the glad songs of the blest, Let Jesus come in-to your heart; If you would en-ter the man-sions of rest, Let Jesus come into your heart.

Chorus

Just now, your doubt-ings give o'er; Just now, re-ject Him no more; Just now, throw

o - pen the door; Let Je - sus come in - to your heart.

My Jesus, I Love Thee 71

William R. Featherstone

Adoniram J. Gordon

1. My Je - sus, I love Thee, I know Thou art mine; For Thee all the
2. I love Thee be - cause Thou hast first lov - ed me, And pur - chased my
3. I'll love Thee in life, I will love Thee in death, And praise Thee as
4. In man - sions of glo - ry and end - less de - light, I'll ev - er a -

fol - lies of sin I re - sign; My gra - cious Re - deem - er, my
par - don on Cal - va - ry's tree; I love Thee for wear - ing the
long as Thou lend - est me breath; And say when the death - dew lies
dore Thee in heav - en so bright; I'll sing with the glit - ter - ing

Sav - iour art Thou; If ev - er I loved Thee, my Je - sus, 'tis now.
thorns on Thy brow; If ev - er I loved Thee, my Je - sus, 'tis now.
cold on my brow, If ev - er I loved Thee, my Je - sus, 'tis now.
crown on my brow, If ev - er I loved Thee, my Je - sus, 'tis now

72 Love Lifted Me

James Rowe

Howard E. Smith

1. I was sink-ing deep in sin, Far from the peace-ful shore, Ver-y deep-ly
2. All my heart to Him I give, Ev-er to Him I'll cling, In His bless-ed
3. Souls in dan-ger, look a-bove, Je-sus com-plete-ly saves; He will lift you

stained with-in, Sink-ing to rise no more; But the Mas-ter of the sea
pres-ence live, Ev-er His prais-es sing. Love so might-y and so true
by His love Out of the an-gry waves. He's the Mas-ter of the sea,

Heard my des-pair-ing cry, From the wa-ters lift-ed me, Now safe am I.
Mer-its my soul's best songs; Faith-ful, lov-ing serv-ice, too, To Him be-longs.
Bil-lows His will o-bey; He your Sav-ior wants to be—Be saved to-day.

Chorus

Love lift-ed me! Love lift-ed me! When noth-ing
e-ven me! e-ven me!

else could help, Love lift-ed me. Love lift-ed me.

My Faith Has Found a Resting Place 73

Lidie H. Edmunds

Norse Air
Arr. by William J. Kirkpatrick

1. My faith has found a rest-ing-place, Not in de-vice nor creed;
2. E - nough for me that Je - sus saves, This ends my fear and doubt;
3. My heart is lean-ing on the Word, The writ-ten Word of God,
4. My great Phy - si - cian heals the sick, The lost He came to save;

I trust the Ev - er - liv - ing One, His wounds for me shall plead.
A sin - ful soul I come to Him, He'll nev - er cast me out.
Sal - va - tion by my Sav - iour's name, Sal - va - tion thro' His blood.
For me His pre-cious blood He shed, For me His Life He gave.

Chorus

I need no oth - er ar - gu-ment, I need no oth - er plea,

It is e - nough that Je - sus died, And that He died for me.

74   Power in the Blood

Lewis E. Jones

Lewis E. Jones

1. Would you be free from the bur-den of sin? There's power in the blood,
2. Would you be free from your pas-sion and pride? There's power in the blood,
3. Would you be whit-er, much whit-er than snow? There's power in the blood,
4. Would you do serv-ice for Je-sus, your King? There's power in the blood,

power in the blood; Would you o'er e-vil a vic-to-ry win? There's
power in the blood; Come for a cleans-ing to Cal-va-ry's tide; There's
power in the blood; Sin-stains are lost in its life-giv-ing flow; There's
power in the blood; Would you live dai-ly His prais-es to sing? There's

Refrain

won-der-ful power in the blood. There is power, power, Won-der-work-ing power
there is

In the blood of the Lamb; There is power, power,
In the blood of the Lamb; there is

Won-der-work-ing power In the pre-cious blood of the Lamb.

Saved, Saved!

Jack P. Scholfield

Jack P. Scholfield

Unison

1. I've found a friend who is all to me, His
2. He saves me from ev - ery sin and harm, Se -
3. When poor and need - y and all a - lone, In

love is ev - er true; I love to tell how He
cures my soul each day; I'm lean - ing strong on His
love He said to me, "Come un - to Me and I'll

rit.

lift - ed me, And what His grace can do for you.
might - y arm; I know He'll guide me all the way.
lead you home, To live with Me e - ter - nal - ly."

Refrain

Saved by His power di - vine, Saved to new life sub - lime!
Saved by His power, Saved to new life,

Life now is sweet and my joy is com - plete, For I'm saved, saved, saved!

76   Thank You, Lord

Seth Sykes &
Bessie Sykes

Seth Sykes &
Bessie Sykes

1. Some thank the Lord for friends and home, For mer-cies sure and sweet;
2. Some thank Him for the flow'rs that grow, Some for the stars that shine;
3. I trust in Him from day to day, I prove His sav-ing grace;

But I would praise Him for His grace— In prayer I would re - peat:
My heart is filled with joy and praise Be - cause I know He's mine.
I'll sing this song of praise to Him Un - til I see His face.

Chorus

Thank you, Lord, for sav-ing my soul, Thank you, Lord, for mak-ing me whole

Thank you, Lord, for giv-ing to me Thy great sal - va-tion so rich and free.

There Is a Fountain

William Cowper

American Melody

1. There is a foun-tain filled with blood Drawn from Im-man-uel's veins,
2. The dy-ing thief re-joiced to see That foun-tain in his day,
3. Dear dy-ing Lamb, Thy pre-cious blood Shall nev-er lose its pow'r,
4. E'er since by faith I saw the stream Thy flow-ing wounds sup-ply,
5. When this poor lisp-ing, stam-m'ring tongue Lies si-lent in the grave,

And sin-ners plunged be-neath that flood Lose all their guilt-y stains:
And there may I, though vile as he, Wash all my sins a-way:
Till all the ran-somed Church of God Be saved to sin no more:
Re-deem-ing love has been my theme And shall be till I die:
Then in a no-bler, sweet-er song, I'll sing Thy pow'r to save:

Lose all their guilt-y stains, Lose all their guilt-y stains;
Wash all my sins a-way, Wash all my sins a-way;
Be saved to sin no more, Be saved to sin no more;
And shall be till I die, And shall be till I die;
I'll sing Thy pow'r to save, I'll sing Thy pow'r to save;

And sin-ners plunged be-neath that flood Lose all their guilt-y stains.
And there may I, though vile as he, Wash all my sins a-way.
Till all the ran-somed Church of God Be saved to sin no more.
Re-deem-ing love has been my theme And shall be till I die.
Then in a no-bler, sweet-er song, I'll sing Thy pow'r to save.

78   'Tis So Sweet to Trust in Jesus

Louisa M. R. Stead   *William J. Kirkpatrick*

1. 'Tis so sweet to trust in Je - sus, Just to take Him at His word,
2. O how sweet to trust in Je - sus, Just to trust His cleans-ing blood,
3. Yes, 'tis sweet to trust in Je - sus, Just from sin and self to cease,
4. I'm so glad I learned to trust Thee, Pre-cious Je - sus, Sav - ior, Friend;

Just to rest up - on His prom-ise, Just to know, "Thus saith the Lord."
Just in sim - ple faith to plunge me 'Neath the heal - ing, cleans-ing flood!
Just from Je - sus sim-ply tak - ing Life and rest and joy and peace.
And I know that Thou art with me, Wilt be with me to the end.

Chorus

Je - sus, Je - sus, how I trust Him! How I've proved Him o'er and o'er!

Je - sus, Je - sus, pre - cious Je - sus! O for grace to trust Him more!

To God Be the Glory

Fanny J. Crosby

William H. Doane

1. To God be the glo - ry, great things He hath done, So loved He the world that He
2. O per - fect re-demp-tion, the pur-chase of blood, To ev - 'ry be - liev - er the
3. Great things He hath taught us, great things He hath done, And great our re-joic-ing thru'

gave us His Son, Who yield - ed His life an a-tone-ment for sin, And o-pened the
prom-ise of God; The vil - est of - fen-der who tru - ly believes, That moment from
Je - sus the Son; But pur - er, and high-er, and great-er will be Our won-der, our

Refrain

life - gate that all may go in.
Je - sus a par-don re-ceives. Praise the Lord, praise the Lord, Let the earth hear His
trans-port, when Je - sus we see.

voice! Praise the Lord, praise the Lord, Let the peo-ple re-joice! O come to the

Fa - ther thru' Je - sus the Son, And give Him the glo-ry; great things He hath done.

Turn Your Eyes upon Jesus

Helen H. Lemmel   *Helen H. Lemmel*

1. O soul, are you wea - ry and troub - led? No light in the
2. Thru' death in - to life ev - er - last - ing He passed, and we
3. His word shall not fail you— He prom - ised; Be - lieve Him, and

dark-ness you see? There's light for a look at the Sav - ior,
fol - low Him there; O - ver us sin no more hath do - min - ion—
all will be well: Then go to a world that is dy - ing,

Refrain

And life more a - bun - dant and free!
For more than con - qu'rors we are! Turn your eyes up - on Je -
His per - fect sal - va - tion to tell!

sus, Look full in His won - der - ful face; And the things of

earth will grow strange-ly dim In the light of His glo - ry and grace.

We Have an Anchor

81

Priscilla J. Owens

William J. Kirkpatrick

1. Will your an-chor hold in the storms of life, When the clouds un - fold
2. It is safe-ly moored,'twill the storm with-stand, For 'tis well se - cured
3. It will firm-ly hold in the straits of fear, When the break-ers have told
4. Then our eyes be - hold thru' the gath'-ring night The cit - y of gold,

their wings of strife? When the strong tides lift, and the ca - bles strain,
by the Sav - ior's hand; And the ca - bles, passed from His heart to mine,
the reef is near; Tho' the tem - pest rave and the wild winds blow,
our har - bor bright, We shall an - chor fast by the heav'n - ly shore,

Refrain

Will your an - chor drift, or firm re - main?
Can de - fy that blast, thru' strength di - vine.
Not an an - gry wave shall our bark o'er - flow.
With the storms all past for - ev - er - more.

We have an an - chor that

keeps the soul Stead - fast and sure while the bil - lows roll, Fas - tened to the

Rock which can - not move, Ground - ed firm and deep in the Sav - ior's love.

82 Victory in Jesus

Eugene M. Bartlett   *Eugene M. Bartlett*

1. I heard an old, old sto - ry, how a Sav - ior came from glo - ry,
2. I heard a - bout His heal - ing, of His cleans-ing pow'r re - veal-ing,
3. I heard a - bout a man-sion He has built for me in glo - ry,

How He gave His life on Cal - va - ry to save a wretch like me;
How He made the lame to walk a - gain and caused the blind to see;
And I heard a - bout the streets of gold be - yond the crys - tal sea,

I heard a - bout His groan-ing, of His pre-cious blood's a - ton-ing,
And then I cried, "Dear Je - sus, come and heal my bro - ken spir-it,"
A - bout the an - gels sing - ing and the old re - demp-tion sto-ry—

Then I re - pent - ed of my sins and won the vic - to - ry.
And some - how Je - sus came and brought to me the vic - to - ry.
And some sweet day I'll sing up there the song of vic - to - ry.

Chorus

O vic - to - ry in Je - sus, My Sav-ior, for - ev - er! He sought me and

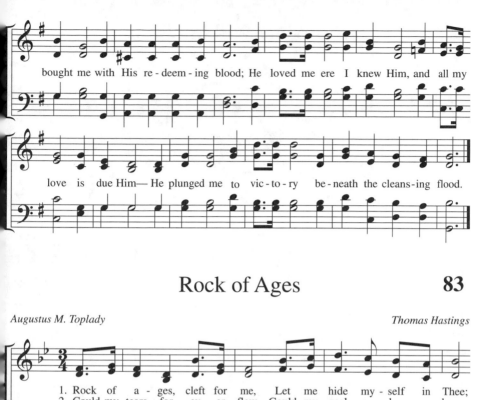

bought me with His re-deem-ing blood; He loved me ere I knew Him, and all my

love is due Him— He plunged me to vic-to-ry be-neath the cleans-ing flood.

Rock of Ages

83

Augustus M. Toplady

Thomas Hastings

1. Rock of a - ges, cleft for me, Let me hide my-self in Thee;
2. Could my tears for - ev - er flow, Could my zeal no lan - guor know,
3. While I draw this fleet-ing breath, When my eyes shall close in death,

Let the wa - ter and the blood, From Thy wound - ed side which flowed,
These for sin could not a - tone— Thou must save, and Thou a - lone:
When I rise to worlds un - known And be - hold Thee on Thy throne,

Be of sin the dou - ble cure, Save from wrath and make me pure.
In my hand no price I bring, Sim - ply to Thy cross I cling.
Rock of A - ges, cleft for me, Let me hide my-self in Thee.

84 Whosoever Will May Come

Philip P. Bliss   *Philip P. Bliss*

1. "Who-so-ev-er hear-eth," shout, shout the sound! Spread the bless-ed ti - dings all the world a - round; Tell the joy-ful news wher-ev - er man is found,

2. Who-so-ev-er com - eth need not de - lay, Now the door is o - pen, en - ter while you may; Je - sus is the true, the on - ly liv - ing Way:

3. "Who-so-ev-er will," the prom-ise is se - cure; "Who - so - ev - er will," for- ev - er must en - dure; "Who-so-ev - er will," 'tis life for - ev - er-more;

Refrain

"Who-so - ev - er will may come." "Who-so - ev - er will, who-so-ev - er will!" Send the proc - la - ma - tion o - ver vale and hill; 'Tis a lov - ing Fa - ther calls the wan-derer home: "Who - so - ev - er will may come."

Guide Me, O Thou Great Jehovah 85

William Williams
Trans. by Peter Williams

John Hughes

1. Guide me, O Thou great Je - ho - vah, Pil - grim through this
2. O - pen now the crys - tal foun - tain, Whence the heal - ing
3. When I tread the verge of Jor - dan, Bid my anx - ious

bar - ren land; I am weak, but Thou art might - y; Hold me with Thy
stream doth flow; Let the fire and cloud - y pil - lar Lead me all my
fears sub - side; Death of death, and hell's De - struc-tion, Land me safe on

pow'r - ful hand; Bread of heav - en, Bread of heav - en,
jour - ney through; Strong De - liv - erer, strong De - liv - erer,
Ca - naan's side; Songs of prais - es, songs of prais - es

Feed me till I want no more, Feed me till I want no more.
Be Thou still my Strength and Shield, Be Thou still my Strength and Shield.
I will ev - er give to Thee, I will ev - er give to Thee.

When Morning Gilds the Skies

From German
Trans. by Edward Caswall

Joseph Barnby

1. When morn - ing gilds the skies, My heart a - wak - ing cries:
2. Does sad - ness fill my mind, A sol - ace here I find:
3. In heaven's e - ter - nal bliss The love - liest strain is this,
4. Be this, while life is mine, My can - ti - cle di - vine,

May Je - sus Christ be praised; A - like at work or prayer
May Je - sus Christ be praised; Or fades my earth - ly bliss,
May Je - sus Christ be praised; The powers of dark - ness fear,
May Je - sus Christ be praised; Be this th' e - ter - nal song,

To Je - sus I re - pair: May Je - sus Christ be praised
My com - fort still is this: May Je - sus Christ be praised
When this sweet chant they hear: May Je - sus Christ be praised
Through all the a - ges on: May Je - sus Christ be praised

Abide with Me

Henry F. Lyte

William H. Mon

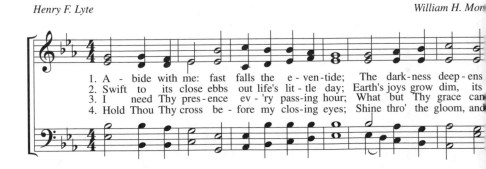

1. A - bide with me: fast falls the e - ven-tide; The dark-ness deep - ens
2. Swift to its close ebbs out life's lit - tle day; Earth's joys grow dim, its
3. I need Thy pres-ence ev - 'ry pass-ing hour; What but Thy grace can
4. Hold Thou Thy cross be - fore my clos-ing eyes; Shine thro' the gloom, and

Lord, with me a - bide: When oth - er help - ers fail, and
glo - ries pass a - way; Change and de - cay in all a -
foil the tempt - er's pow'r? Who like Thy - self my guide and
point me to the skies: Heav'n's morn - ing breaks and earth's vain

com - forts flee, Help of the help - less, O a - bide with me!
round I see: O Thou who chang - est not, a - bide with me!
stay can be? Thru' cloud and sun - shine, O a - bide with me!
shad - ows flee: In life, in death, O Lord, a - bide with me!

I Need Thee Every Hour

88

Annie S. Hawks

Robert Lowry

1. I need Thee ev-ery hour, Most gra - cious Lord; No ten - der voice like
2. I need Thee ev-ery hour, Stay Thou near by; Temp - ta - tions lose their
3. I need Thee ev-ery hour, In joy or pain; Come quick - ly and a -
4. I need Thee ev-ery hour, Most Ho - ly One; O make me Thine in -

Chorus

Thine Can peace af - ford.
power When Thou art nigh.
bide, Or life is vain. I need Thee, O I need Thee; Ev - ery hour I
deed, Thou bless - ed Son!

need Thee; O bless me now, my Sav - iour, I come to Thee!

89 I Am Thine, O Lord

Fanny J. Crosby   *William H. Doane*

1. I am Thine, O Lord— I have heard Thy voice, And it told Thy
2. Con - se - crate me now to Thy serv - ice, Lord, By the pow'r of
3. O the pure de - light of a sin - gle hour That be - fore Thy
4. There are depths of love that I can - not know Till I cross the

love to me; But I long to rise in the arms of faith
grace di - vine; Let my soul look up with a stead - fast hope
throne I spend, When I kneel in pray'r and with Thee, my God,
nar - row sea; There are heights of joy that I may not reach

Refrain

And be clos - er drawn to Thee.
And my will be lost in Thine.   Draw me near - er,   near - er,
I com - mune as friend with friend.   near - er, near-er,
Till I rest in peace with Thee.

bless - ed Lord, To the cross where Thou hast died; Draw me near - er,

near - er, near - er, bless - ed Lord, To Thy pre - cious, bleed - ing side.

In the Garden

C. Austin Miles

C. Austin Miles

1. I come to the gar-den a - lone, While the dew is still on the
2. He speaks, and the sound of His voice Is so sweet the birds hush their
3. I'd stay in the gar-den with Him Though the night a - round me be

ros - es; And the voice I hear, fall - ing on my ear; The
sing - ing, And the mel - o - dy that He gave to me, With-
fall - ing, But He bids me go; through the voice of woe, His

Refrain

Son of God dis - clos - es.
in my heart is ring - ing. And He walks with me, and He
voice to me is call - ing.

talks with me, And He tells me I am His own, And the

joy we share as we tar - ry there, None oth - er has ev - er known.

91 More Like the Master

Charles H. Gabriel Alt.

Charles H. Gabriel

1. More like the Mas-ter I would ev-er be, More of His meek-ness,
2. More like the Mas-ter is my dai-ly prayer; More strength to car-ry
3. More like the Mas-ter I would live and grow; More of His love to

more hu-mil-i-ty; More zeal to la-bor, more cour-age to be true,
cross-es I must bear; More ear-nest ef-fort to lead some soul to Him;
oth-ers I would show; More self-de-ni-al, like His in Gal-i-lee,

Refrain

More con-se-cra-tion for work He bids me do. Take Thou my
More of His Spir-it, the wan-der-er to win. Take my heart, O
More like my Sav-ior I long to ev-er be. Take my heart, O

heart, I would be Thine a-lone; Take Thou my life and
take my heart, I would be Thine a-lone; Take my life, O take my life and

make it all Thine own; Purge me from sin, O Lord, I now im
make it all Thine own; Purge Thou me from ev-'ry sin, O Lord, I

plore,   Wash   me   and   keep   me   Thine for-ev-er - more.
now im-plore,   Wash and keep, O   wash and keep me   Thine for-ev-er - more.

Jesus, Savior, Pilot Me   92

Edward Hopper   *John E. Gould*

1. Je - sus, Sav-ior, pi - lot me   O - ver   life's   tem - pes-tuous   sea;
2. As   a   moth-er stills her child, Thou canst hush   the   o - cean   wild;
3. When at   last I   near the shore, And   the   fear - ful break-ers   roar

Un - known   waves be - fore me   roll,   Hid - ing   rock   and treach-'rous
Bois - terous   waves o - bey Thy   will   When Thou say'st   to   them, "Be
'Twixt me   and   the   peace-ful   rest,   Then,   while   lean - ing   on   Thy

shoal;   Chart and com-pass came from Thee: Je - sus, Sav - ior, pi - lot   me.
still!"   Won-drous Sov-'reign of   the   sea, Je - sus, Sav - ior, pi - lot   me.
breast,   May I   hear Thee say   to   me, "Fear not, I   will pi - lot thee."

More about Jesus

Eliza E. Hewitt

John R. Swene

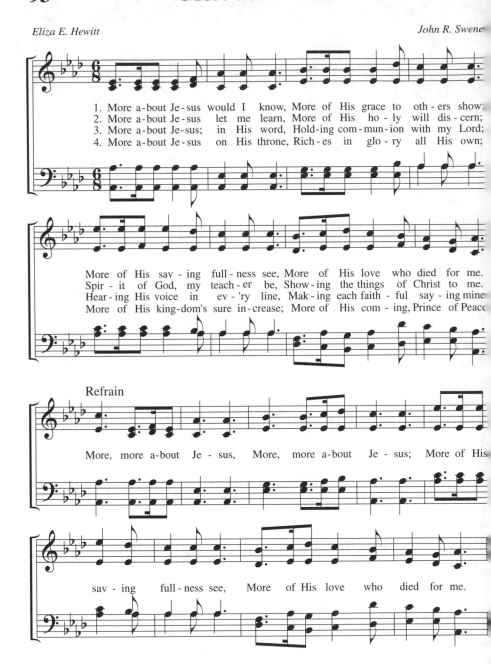

1. More a-bout Je-sus would I know, More of His grace to oth-ers show;
2. More a-bout Je-sus let me learn, More of His ho-ly will dis-cern;
3. More a-bout Je-sus; in His word, Hold-ing com-mun-ion with my Lord;
4. More a-bout Je-sus on His throne, Rich-es in glo-ry all His own;

More of His sav-ing full-ness see, More of His love who died for me.
Spir-it of God, my teach-er be, Show-ing the things of Christ to me.
Hear-ing His voice in ev-'ry line, Mak-ing each faith-ful say-ing mine.
More of His king-dom's sure in-crease; More of His com-ing, Prince of Peace

Refrain

More, more a-bout Je-sus, More, more a-bout Je-sus; More of His

sav-ing full-ness see, More of His love who died for me.

Savior, Like a Shepherd Lead Us

94

Dorothy A. Thrupp   *William B. Bradbury*

1. Sav - ior, like a shep-herd lead us, Much we need Thy ten - der care;
2. We are Thine; do Thou be - friend us, Be the Guard-ian of our way;
3. Thou hast prom-ised to re - ceive us, Poor and sin - ful though we be;
4. Ear - ly let us seek Thy fa - vor; Ear - ly let us do Thy will;

In Thy pleas-ant pas-tures feed us, For our use Thy folds pre - pare:
Keep Thy flock, from sin de - fend us, Seek us when we go a - stray:
Thou hast mer - cy to re - lieve us, Grace to cleanse, and power to free:
Bless - ed Lord and on - ly Sav - ior, With Thy love our bos - oms fill:

Bless - ed Je - sus, Bless - ed Je - sus, Thou hast bought us, Thine we are;
Bless - ed Je - sus, Bless - ed Je - sus, Hear, O hear us when we pray;
Bless - ed Je - sus, Bless - ed Je - sus, Ear - ly let us turn to Thee;
Bless - ed Je - sus, Bless - ed Je - sus, Thou hast loved us, love us still;

Bless - ed Je - sus, Bless-ed Je - sus, Thou hast bought us, Thine we are.
Bless - ed Je - sus, Bless-ed Je - sus, Hear, O hear us when we pray.
Bless - ed Je - sus, Bless-ed Je - sus, Ear - ly let us turn to Thee.
Bless - ed Je - sus, Bless-ed Je - sus, Thou hast loved us, love us still.

95

Near the Cross

Fanny J. Crosby

William H. Doane

1. Je - sus, keep me near the cross, There a pre - cious foun-tain Free to
2. Near the cross, a trem - bling soul, Love and mer - cy found me; There the
3. Near the cross! O Lamb of God, Bring its scenes be-fore me; Help me
4. Near the cross I'll watch and wait, Hop - ing, trust - ing, ev - er, Till I

Chorus

all— a heal - ing stream, Flows from Cal-v'ry's moun-tain.
Bright and Morn-ing Star Sheds its beams a - round me.
walk from day to day, With its shad-ows o'er me. In the cross, in the cross,
reach the gold - en strand, Just be - yond the riv - er.

Be my glo - ry ev - er; Till my rap-tured soul shall find Rest be-yond the riv - er.

96

Near to the Heart of God

Cleland B. McAfee

Cleland B. McAfee

1. There is a place of qui - et rest, Near to the heart of God, A place where
2. There is a place of com-fort sweet, Near to the heart of God, A place where
3. There is a place of full re - lease, Near to the heart of God, A place where

Chorus

sin can-not mo-lest, Near to the heart of God.
we our Sav-ior meet, Near to the heart of God. O Je-sus, blest Re-deem-er,
all is joy and peace, Near to the heart of God.

Sent from the heart of God, Hold us who wait be-fore Thee Near to the heart of God.

Nearer, My God, to Thee 97

Sarah F. Adams

Lowell Mason

1. Near - er, my God, to Thee, Near - er to Thee! E'en tho it
2. Though like the wan - der - er, The sun gone down, Dark - ness be
3. There let the way ap - pear, Steps un - to heav'n; All that Thou
4. Then with my wak - ing thoughts, Bright with Thy praise, Out of my
5. Or if on joy - ful wing, Cleav - ing the sky, Sun, moon, and

be a cross That rais - eth me; Still all my song shall be,
o - ver me, My rest a stone, Yet in my dreams I'd be
send - est me, In mer - cy giv'n— An - gels to beck - on me
ston - y griefs, Beth - el I raise; So by my woes to be
stars for - got, Up - ward I fly, Still all my song shall be,

Near - er, my God, to Thee, Near - er, my God, to Thee, Near - er to Thee!

98 The Solid Rock

Edward Mote   *William B. Bradbury*

1. My hope is built on noth-ing less Than Je-sus' blood and right-eous-ness.
2. When dark-ness veils His love-ly face, I rest on His un-chang-ing grace.
3. His oath, His cov-e-nant, His blood Sup-port me in the whelm-ing flood.
4. When He shall come with trum-pet sound, O may I then in Him be found.

I dare not trust the sweet-est frame, But whol-ly lean on Je-sus' name.
In ev-'ry high and storm-y gale My an-chor holds with-in the veil.
When all a-round my soul gives way, He then is all my hope and stay.
Dressed in His right-eous-ness a-lone, Fault-less to stand be-fore the throne.

Refrain

On Christ, the sol-id Rock, I stand— All oth-er ground is

sink-ing sand, All oth-er ground is sink-ing sand.

Sweet Hour of Prayer

William W. Walford

William B. Bradbury

1. Sweet hour of prayer, sweet hour of prayer, That calls me from a world of care
2. Sweet hour of prayer, sweet hour of prayer, Thy wings shall my pe - ti - tion bear
3. Sweet hour of prayer, sweet hour of prayer, May I thy con - so - la - tion share,

And bids me at my Fa - ther's throne Make all my wants and wish - es known!
To Him whose truth and faith - ful - ness En - gage the wait - ing soul to bless;
Till from Mount Pis - gah's loft - y height I view my home and take my flight:

In sea - sons of dis - tress and grief My soul has of - ten found re - lief,
And since He bids me seek His face, Be - lieve His Word and trust His grace,
This robe of flesh I'll drop, and rise To sieze the ev - er - last - ing prize,

And oft es - caped the tempt-er's snare By thy re - turn, sweet hour of prayer.
I'll cast on Him my ev - 'ry care, And wait for thee, sweet hour of prayer.
And shout, while pass - ing thru the air, "Fare-well, fare-well, sweet hour of prayer!"

100

Tell It to Jesus

Jeremiah E. Rankin

Edmund S. Loren

1. Are you wea - ry, are you heav - y - heart - ed? Tell it to Je - sus,
2. Do the tears flow down your cheeks un - bid - den? Tell it to Je - sus,
3. Do you fear the gath - 'ring clouds of sor - row? Tell it to Je - sus,
4. Are you trou - bled at the thought of dy - ing? Tell it to Je - sus,

Tell it to Je - sus; Are you griev - ing o - ver joys de - part - ed?
Tell it to Je - sus; Have you sins that to men's eyes are hid - den
Tell it to Je - sus; Are you anx - ious what shall be to - mor - row
Tell it to Je - sus; For Christ's com - ing king - dom are you sigh - ing

Chorus

Tell it to Je - sus a - lone. Tell it to Je - sus, tell it to

Je - sus, He is a friend that's well known; You've no oth - er

such a friend or broth - er, Tell it to Je - sus a - lone.

Daniel W. Whittle   *James McGranahan*

1. There shall be show-ers of bless-ing— This is the prom-ise of love;
2. There shall be show-ers of bless-ing— Pre-cious, re-viv-ing a-gain;
3. There shall be show-ers of bless-ing— Send them up-on us, O Lord!
4. There shall be show-ers of bless-ing— Oh, that to-day they might fall,
5. There shall be show-ers of bless-ing— If we but trust and o-bey;

There shall be sea-sons re-fresh-ing Sent from the Sav-iour a-bove.
O-ver the hills and the val-leys Sound of a-bun-dance of rain.
Grant to us now a re-fresh-ing; Come, and now hon-or Thy Word.
Now as to God we're con-fess-ing, Now as on Je-sus we call!
There shall be sea-sons re-fresh-ing, If we let God have His way.

Refrain

Show - - - ers of bless - ing,

Show-ers, show-ers of bless - ing, Show-ers of bless-ing we need;

Mer-cy drops round us are fall-ing, But for the show-ers we plead.

102   What a Friend We Have in Jesus

Joseph Scriven   *Charles C. Converse*

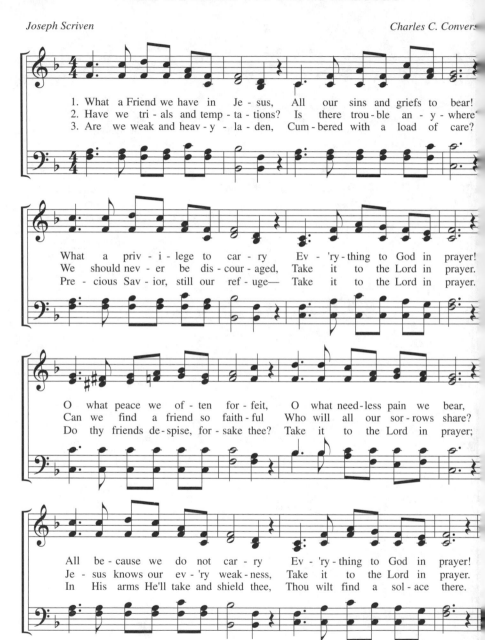

1. What a Friend we have in Je - sus, All our sins and griefs to bear!
2. Have we tri - als and temp - ta - tions? Is there trou - ble an - y - where?
3. Are we weak and heav - y - la - den, Cum - bered with a load of care?

What a priv - i - lege to car - ry Ev - 'ry - thing to God in prayer!
We should nev - er be dis - cour - aged, Take it to the Lord in prayer.
Pre - cious Sav - ior, still our ref - uge— Take it to the Lord in prayer.

O what peace we of - ten for - feit, O what need - less pain we bear,
Can we find a friend so faith - ful Who will all our sor - rows share?
Do thy friends de - spise, for - sake thee? Take it to the Lord in prayer;

All be - cause we do not car - ry Ev - 'ry - thing to God in prayer!
Je - sus knows our ev - 'ry weak - ness, Take it to the Lord in prayer.
In His arms He'll take and shield thee, Thou wilt find a sol - ace there.

Be Still, My Soul

Katherina von Schlegel
Trans. by Jane L. Borthwick

Jean Sibelius

1. Be still, my soul: the Lord is on thy side; Bear pa - tient - ly the
2. Be still, my soul: thy God doth un - der - take To guide the fu - ture
3. Be still, my soul: the hour is has - tening on When we shall be for -

cross of grief or pain; Leave to thy God to or - der and pro - vide;
as He has the past. Thy hope, thy con - fi - dence let noth - ing shake;
ev - er with the Lord, When dis - ap - point - ment, grief, and fear are gone,

In ev - ery change He faith - ful will re - main. Be still, my soul: thy
All now mys - te - rious shall be bright at last. Be still, my soul: the
Sor - row for - got, love's pur - est joys re - stored. Be still, my soul: when

best, thy heav'n - ly Friend Through thorn - y ways leads to a joy - ful end.
waves and winds still know His voice who ruled them while He dwelt be - low.
change and tears are past, All safe and bless - ed we shall meet at last.

104
Come Thou Fount

Robert Robinson   *John Wyeth*

1. Come, Thou Fount of ev-ery bless-ing, Tune my heart to sing Thy grace;
2. Here I raise my sign of vic-tory; Hith-er by Thy help I'm come;
3. O to grace how great a debt-or Dai-ly I'm con-strained to be!

Streams of mer-cy, nev-er ceas-ing, Call for songs of loud-est praise.
And I know, by Thy good pleas-ure, Safe-ly to ar-rive at home.
Let Thy good-ness, like a fet-ter, Bind my wan-d'ring heart to Thee.

Teach me some me-lo-dious son-net Sung by flam-ing tongues a-bove.
Je-sus sought me when a stran-ger, Wan-d'ring from the fold of God;
Prone to wan-der, Lord, I feel it, Prone to leave the God I love;

Praise the mount! I'm fixed up-on it, Mount of Thy re-deem-ing love.
He, to res-cue me from dan-ger, In-ter-posed His pre-cious blood.
Here's my heart, O take and seal it, Seal it for Thy courts a-bove.

Day by Day

Lina Sandell Berg
Trans. by Andrew L. Skoog

Oscar Ahnfelt

1. Day by day and with each pass-ing mo-ment, Strength I find to
2. Ev - 'ry day the Lord Him-self is near me With a spe - cial
3. Help me then in ev - 'ry trib - u - la - tion So to trust Thy

meet my tri - als here; Trust-ing in my Fa - ther's wise be - stow-ment,
mer - cy for each hour; All my cares He fain would bear, and cheer me,
prom-is - es, O Lord, That I lose not faith's sweet con - so - la - tion

I've no cause to wor - ry or for fear. He whose heart is kind be-
He whose name is Coun - sel - lor and Pow'r. The pro - tec - tion of His
Of - fered me with - in Thy ho - ly word. Help me, Lord, when toil and

yond all meas - ure Gives un - to each day what He deems best— Lov - ing-
child and treas - ure Is a charge that on Him-self He laid; "As thy
trou - ble meet-ing, E'er to take, as from a fa - ther's hand, One by

ly, its part of pain and pleas-ure, Min-gling toil with peace and rest.
days, thy strength shall be in meas-ure," This the pledge to me He made.
one, the days, the mo-ments fleet - ing, Till I reach the prom - ised land.

106 Faith Is the Victory

John H. Yates

Ira D. Sank[e]

1. En-camped a-long the hills of light, Ye Chris-tian sol-diers, rise,
2. His ban-ner o-ver us is love, Our sword the Word of God;
3. On ev-ery hand the foe we find Drawn up in dread ar-ray;
4. To him that o-ver-comes the foe White rai-ment shall be given;

And press the bat-tle ere the night Shall veil the glow-ing skies.
We tread the road the saints a-bove With shouts of tri-umph trod.
Let tents of ease be left be-hind, And on-ward to the fray;
Be-fore the an-gels he shall know His name con-fessed in heaven.

A-gainst the foe in vales be-low, Let all our strength be hurled;
By faith they, like a whirl-wind's breath, Swept on o'er ev-ery field;
Sal-va-tion's hel-met on each head, With truth all girt a-bout,
Then on-ward from the hills of light, Our hearts with love a-flame,

Faith is the vic-to-ry, we know, That o-ver-comes the world.
The faith by which they con-quered death Is still our shin-ing shield.
The earth shall trem-ble 'neath our tread And ech-o with our shout.
We'll van-quish all the hosts of night In Je-sus' con-quering name.

Refrain

Faith is the vic-to-ry! Faith is the vic-to-ry!

Oh, glo-ri-ous vic-to-ry That o-ver-comes the world.

Faith of Our Fathers 107

Frederick W. Faber

Henri F. Hemy

1. Faith of our fa - thers, liv - ing still In spite of dun - geon,
2. Our fa - thers, chained in pris - on dark, Were still in heart and
3. Faith of our fa - thers! We will love Both friend and foe in

fire, and sword! Oh, how our hearts beat high with joy
con - science free. Lord, grant their chil - dren strength and love,
all our strife; And preach thee, too, as love knows how

Refrain

When-e'er we hear that glo - rious word:
Like them, to live and die for Thee. Faith of our fa-thers,
By kind - ly words and vir - tuous life.

ho - ly faith! We will be true to thee till death.

108 He Leadeth Me

Joseph H. Gilmore

William B. Bradbury

1. He lead - eth me— Oh, bless-ed thought! Oh, words with heav'n-ly com-fort fraught!
2. Some-times 'mid scenes of deep-est gloom, Some-times where E-den's bow-ers bloom,
3. Lord, I would clasp Thy hand in mine, Nor ev - er mur-mur nor re-pine,
4. And when my task on earth is done, When, by Thy grace, the vic-t'ry's won,

What - e'er I do, wher-e'er I be, Still 'tis God's hand that lead-eth me.
By wa - ters calm, o'er trou-bled sea, Still 'tis His hand that lead-eth me.
Con - tent, what-ev - er lot I see, Since 'tis my God that lead-eth me.
E'en death's cold wave I will not flee, Since God through Jor - dan lead-eth me.

Refrain

He lead-eth me, He lead - eth me; By His own hand He lead-eth me.

His faith-ful fol - l'wer I would be, For by His hand He lead - eth me.

Higher Ground

Johnson Oatman, Jr.   *Charles H. Gabriel*

1. I'm press-ing on the up-ward way, New heights I'm gain-ing ev-ery day;
2. I want to live a-bove the world, Though Sa-tan's darts at me are hurled;
3. I want to scale the ut-most height And catch a gleam of glo-ry bright;

Still pray-ing as I on-ward bound, "Lord, plant my feet on high-er ground."
For faith has caught the joy-ful sound, The song of saints on high-er ground.
But still I'll pray till heaven I've found, "Lord, lead me on to high-er ground."

Refrain

Lord, lift me up, and let me stand By faith on heav-en's ta-ble land;

A high-er plane than I have found, Lord, plant my feet on high-er ground.

110   How Firm a Foundation

"K" in Rippon's Selection of Hymns   Mercer's Cluster of Spiritual Songs

1. How firm a foun - da - tion, ye saints of the Lord,
2. "Fear not, I am with thee; O be not dis - mayed,
3. "When through fier - y tri - als thy path - way shall lie,
4. "The soul that on Je - sus hath leaned for re - pose

Is laid for your faith in His ex - cel - lent Word!
For I am thy God, and will still give thee aid;
My grace, all - suf - fi - cient, shall be thy sup - ply:
I will not, I will not de - sert to his foes;

What more can He say than to you He hath said,
I'll strength - en thee, help thee, and cause thee to stand,
The flame shall not hurt thee; I on - ly de - sign
That soul, though all hell should en - deav - or to shake,

To you who for ref - uge to Je - sus have fled?
Up - held by my right - eous, om - nip - o - tent hand.
Thy dross to con - sume, and thy gold to re - fine.
I'll nev - er, no, nev - er, no, nev - er for - sake!"

It Is Well with My Soul

Horatio G. Spafford   *Philip P. Bliss*

1. When peace like a riv - er at - tend - eth my way, When
2. Though Sa - tan should buf - fet, though tri - als should come, Let
3. My sin— oh, the bliss of this glo - ri - ous thought— My
4. And, Lord, haste the day when the faith shall be sight, The

sor - rows like sea bil - lows roll, What - ev - er my lot, Thou hast
this blest as - sur - ance con - trol, That Christ hath re - gard - ed my
sin, not in part but the whole, Is nailed to His cross and I
clouds be rolled back as a scroll, The trump shall re - sound, and the

taught me to say, "It is well, it is well with my soul."
help - less es - tate, And hath shed His own blood for my soul.
bear it no more! Praise the Lord, praise the Lord, O my soul!
Lord shall de - scend! E - ven so— it is well with my soul!

Refrain

It is well   with my soul;   it is well, it is well with my soul!
It is well   with my soul;

112 My Anchor Holds

W. C. Martin

Daniel B. Towner

1. Though the an-gry surg-es roll On my tem-pest-driv-en soul,
2. Might-y tides a-bout me sweep, Per-ils lurk with-in the deep,
3. I can feel the an-chor fast As I meet each sud-den blast,
4. Troub-les al-most 'whelm the soul; Griefs like bil-lows o'er me roll;

I am peace-ful, for I know, Wild-ly though the winds may blow,
An-gry clouds o'er-shade the sky, And the tem-pest ris-es high;
And the ca-ble, though un-seen, Bears the heav-y strain be-tween;
Temp-ters seek to lure a-stray; Storms ob-scure the light of day:

I've an an-chor safe and sure, That can ev-er-more en-dure.
Still I stand the tem-pest's shock, For my an-chor grips the Rock.
Through the storm I safe-ly ride, Till the turn-ing of the tide.
But in Christ I can be bold, I've an an-chor that shall hold.

Chorus

And it holds, my an-chor holds; Blow your wild-est, then, O
And it holds, my an-chor holds; Blow your wild-est,

gale, On my bark so small and frail; By His grace I shall not
then, O gale,

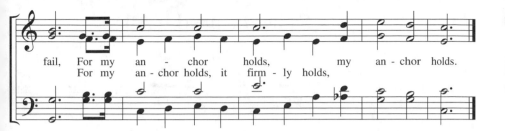

fail, For my an - chor holds, my an - chor holds.
For my an - chor holds, it firm - ly holds,

Leaning on the Everlasting Arms 113

Elisha A. Hoffman
Anthony J. Showalter

1. What a fel-low-ship, what a joy di - vine, Lean-ing on the ev-er - last-ing arms;
2. Oh, how sweet to walk in this pil-grim way, Lean-ing on the ev-er - last-ing arms;
3. What have I to dread, what have I to fear, Lean-ing on the ev-er - last-ing arms?

What a bless-ed-ness, what a peace is mine, Lean-ing on the ev-er - last-ing arms.
Oh, how bright the path grows from day to day, Lean-ing on the ev-er - last-ing arms.
I have bless-ed peace with my Lord so near, Lean-ing on the ev-er - last-ing arms.

Refrain

Lean - ing, lean - ing, Safe and se-cure from all a-larms;
Lean-ing on Je-sus, lean-ing on Je-sus,

Lean - ing, lean - ing, Lean-ing on the ev-er - last-ing arms.
Lean-ing on Je-sus, lean-ing on Je-sus,

114   My Father Planned It All

H. H. Pierson

Alfred B. Smith

1. What tho' the way be lone-ly And dark the shad-ows fall;
2. There may be sun-shine to-mor-row, Shad-ows may break and flee;
3. He guides my falt'-ring foot-steps A-long the wea-ry way,
4. A day of light and glad-ness On which no shade will fall:

I know wher-e'er it lead-eth, My Fa-ther planned it all.
'Twill be the way He choos-es, The Fa-ther's plan for me.
For well He knows the path-way Will lead to end-less day.
'Tis this at last a-waits me— My Fa-ther planned it all.

Chorus

I sing thru' the shade and the sun-shine, I'll trust Him what-ev-er be-fall;
be-fall;

I sing for I can-not be si-lent— My Fa-ther planned it all.
it all.

Standing on the Promises

R. Kelso Carter   R. Kelso Carter

1. Stand-ing on the prom-is-es of Christ my King, Thru e - ter - nal a - ges
2. Stand-ing on the prom-is-es that can - not fail, When the howl - ing storms of
3. Stand-ing on the prom-is-es of Christ the Lord, Bound to Him e - ter - nal-
4. Stand-ing on the prom-is-es I can - not fall, Lis - t'ning ev - 'ry mo - ment

let His prais - es ring; Glo - ry in the high - est I will shout and sing,
doubt and fear as - sail, By the liv - ing word of God I shall pre - vail,
ly by love's strong cord, O - ver - com - ing dai - ly with the Spir - it's sword,
to the Spir - it's call, Rest - ing in my Sav - ior as my all in all,

Chorus

Stand-ing on the prom - is - es of God. Stand - ing, stand -
Stand-ing on the prom-is-es, stand-ing on the

ing, Stand-ing on the prom-is - es of God my Sav - ior; Stand -
prom-is-es, Stand-ing on the

ing, stand - ing, I'm stand - ing on the prom - is - es of God.
prom-is-es, stand-ing on the prom - is - es,

116 Surely Goodness and Mercy

John W. Peterson
& Alfred B. Smith

Alfred B. Smith &
John W. Peterson

1. A pil - grim was I, and a - wan - d'ring, In the cold night of
2. He re - stor - eth my soul when I'm wea - ry, He giv - eth me
3. When I walk thru the dark lone - some val - ley, My Sav - ior will

sin I did roam, When Je - sus the kind Shep - herd found me, And
strength day by day; He leads me be - side the still wa - ters, He
walk with me there; And safe - ly His great hand will lead me To the

Chorus

now I am on my way home.
guards me each step of the way.   Sure - ly good - ness and mer - cy shall
man - sions He's gone to pre - pare.

fol - low me All the days, all the days of my life; Sure - ly good - ness

and mer - cy shall fol - low me All the days, all the days of my life.

Come, Ye Thankful People, Come 117

Henry Alford
Alt. by Hugh Hartshorne

George J. Elvey

1. Come, ye thank-ful peo - ple, come, Raise the song of har - vest - home;
2. All the bless-ings of the field, All the stores the gar - dens yield;
3. These to Thee, our God, we owe, Source whence all our bless - ings flow;

All is safe - ly gath - ered in, Ere the win - ter storms be - gin;
All the fruits in full sup - ply, Ri - pened 'neath the sum - mer sky;
And for these our souls shall raise Grate - ful vows and sol - emn praise.

God, our Mak - er, doth pro - vide For our wants to be sup - plied;
All that spring with boun - teous hand Scat - ters o'er the smil - ing land;
Come, then, thank-ful peo - ple, come, Raise the song of har - vest - home;

Come to God's own tem - ple, come, Raise the song of har - vest - home.
All that lib - eral au - tumn pours From her rich o'er - flow - ing stores:
Come to God's own tem - ple, come, Raise the song of har - vest - home.

118   Now Thank We All Our God

Martin Rinkard
Trans. by Catherine Winkworth

Johann Cruger

1. Now thank we all our God With heart and hands and voi - ces,
2. O may this boun - teous God Through all our life be near us,
3. All praise and thanks to God The Fa - ther now be giv - en,

Who won - drous things hath done, In Whom His world re - joi - ces,
With ev - er - joy - ful hearts And bless - ed peace to cheer us;
The Son, and Him Who reigns With Them in high - est heav - en,

Who, from our moth - ers' arms, Hath blessed us on our way
And keep us in His grace, And guide us when per - plexed,
The one e - ter - nal God, Whom earth and heaven a - dore;

With count - less gifts of love, And still is ours to - day.
And free us from all ills In this world and the next.
For thus it was, is now, And shall be ev - er - more.

Thanks to God! 119

August Ludvig Storm
Freely translated by Norman Johnson

John Alfred Hultman
Arr. by Norman Johnson

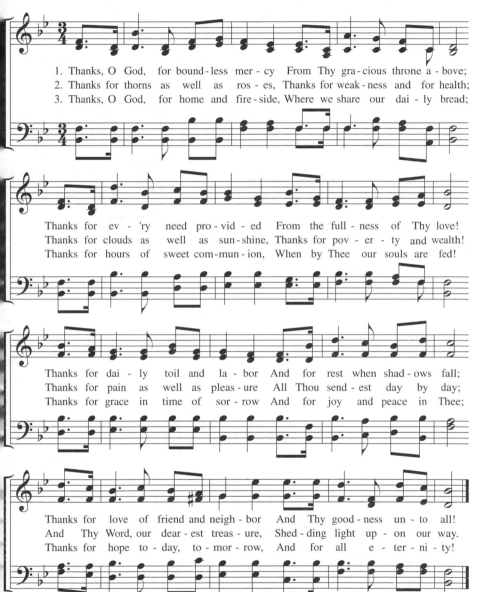

1. Thanks, O God, for bound-less mer-cy From Thy gra-cious throne a-bove;
2. Thanks for thorns as well as ros-es, Thanks for weak-ness and for health;
3. Thanks, O God, for home and fire-side, Where we share our dai-ly bread;

Thanks for ev-'ry need pro-vid-ed From the full-ness of Thy love!
Thanks for clouds as well as sun-shine, Thanks for pov-er-ty and wealth!
Thanks for hours of sweet com-mun-ion, When by Thee our souls are fed!

Thanks for dai-ly toil and la-bor And for rest when shad-ows fall;
Thanks for pain as well as pleas-ure All Thou send-est day by day;
Thanks for grace in time of sor-row And for joy and peace in Thee;

Thanks for love of friend and neigh-bor And Thy good-ness un-to all!
And Thy Word, our dear-est treas-ure, Shed-ding light up-on our way.
Thanks for hope to-day, to-mor-row, And for all e-ter-ni-ty!

120 God Will Take Care of You

Civilla D. Martin

W. Stillman Martin

1. Be not dis - mayed what - e'er be - tide, God will take care of you;
2. Through days of toil when heart doth fail, God will take care of you;
3. All you may need He will pro - vide, God will take care of you;
4. No mat - ter what may be the test, God will take care of you;

Be - neath His wings of love a - bide, God will take care of you.
When dan - gers fierce your path as - sail, God will take care of you.
Noth - ing you ask will be de - nied, God will take care of you.
Lean, wea - ry one, up - on His breast, God will take care of you.

Refrain

God will take care of you, Through ev - ery day, O'er all the way;

He will take care of you, God will take care of you.
take care of you.

He Hideth My Soul

121

Fanny J. Crosby

William J. Kirkpatrick

1. A won - der - ful Sav - ior is Je - sus my Lord, A won - der - ful
2. A won - der - ful Sav - ior is Je - sus my Lord— He tak - eth my
3. With num - ber - less bless - ings each mo - ment He crowns, And, filled with His
4. When clothed in His bright - ness trans - port - ed I rise To meet Him in

Sav - ior to me; He hid - eth my soul in the cleft of the rock, Where
bur - den a - way; He hold - eth me up and I shall not be moved, He
full - ness di - vine, I sing in my rap - ture, "O glo - ry to God For
clouds of the sky, His per - fect sal - va - tion, His won - der - ful love, I'll

Chorus

riv - ers of pleas - ure I see.
giv - eth me strength as my day.
such a Re - deem - er as mine!" He hid - eth my soul in the cleft of the rock
shout with the mil - lions on high.

That shad - ows a dry, thirst - y land; He hid - eth my life in the depths of His love,

And cov - ers me there with His hand, And cov - ers me there with His hand.

122   Like a River Glorious

Frances Ridley Havergal

James Mountain

1. Like a riv - er glo - rious Is God's per - fect peace, O - ver
2. Hid - den in the hol - low Of His bless - ed hand, Nev - er
3. Ev - ery joy or tri - al Fall - eth from a - bove, Traced up -

all vic - to - rious In its bright in - crease; Per - fect, yet it
foe can fol - low, Nev - er trai - tor stand. Not a surge of
on our di - al By the Sun of love. We may trust Him

flow - eth Full - er ev - ery day; Per - fect, yet it grow - eth
wor - ry, Not a shade of care, Not a blast of hur - ry
ful - ly— All for us to do; They who trust Him whol - ly

Refrain

Deep - er all the way.
Touch the spir - it there. Stayed up - on Je - ho - vah Hearts are
Find Him whol - ly true.

ful - ly blest, Find - ing, as He prom - ised, Per - fect peace and rest.

Under His Wings

William O. Cushing   *Ira D. Sankey*

1. Un - der His wings I am safe - ly a - bid - ing, Tho the night
2. Un - der His wings, what a ref - uge in sor - row! How the heart
3. Un - der His wings, O what pre - cious en - joy - ment! There will I

deep - ens and tem - pests are wild; Still I can trust Him— I
yearn - ing - ly turns to His rest! Oft - en when earth has no
hide till life's tri - als are o'er; Shel - tered, pro - tect - ed, no

know He will keep me, He has re - deemed me and I am His child.
balm for my heal - ing, There I find com - fort and there I am blest.
e - vil can harm me, Rest - ing in Je - sus I'm safe ev - er - more.

Chorus

Un - der His wings, un - der His wings, Who from His love can sev - er?

Un - der His wings my soul shall a - bide, Safe - ly a - bide for - ev - er.

124 Are Ye Able?

Earl Marlatt

Henry S. Mason

1. "Are ye a-ble," said the Mas - ter, "To be cru - ci - fied with me?"
2. "Are ye a-ble to re - lin-quish Pur - ple dreams of power and fame,
3. "Are ye a-ble to re-mem-ber When a thief lifts up his eyes,
4. "Are ye a-ble, when the shad-ows Close a - round you with the sod,
5. "Are ye a-ble?" still the Mas - ter Whis-pers down e - ter - ni - ty,

"Yea," the stur - dy dream-ers an-swered, "To the death we fol - low Thee."
To go down in - to the gar - den, Or to die a death of shame?"
That his par-doned soul is wor - thy Of a place in Par - a - dise?"
To be - lieve that spir - it tri - umphs To com - mend your soul to God?"
And he - ro - ic spir-its an - swer, Now, as then, in Gal - i - lee:

Refrain

"Lord, we are a - ble." Our spir - its are Thine. Re - mold them, make us, Like Thee, di - vine. Thy guid - ing ra - diance A - bove us shall be A bea - con to God, To love and loy - al - ty.

A Flag to Follow

125

John W. Peterson

John W. Peterson

1. I sought a flag to fol - low, A cause for which to stand, I sought a val -
2. I sought a ring-ing an - swer For all my doubts in - side, A torch of truth
3. I sought for sat - is - fac - tion For yearn-ings deep with - in, I sought for full

iant lead - er Who could my love com-mand; I sought a stir-ring challenge, Some
up - lift - ed, My search-ing steps to guide; I sought a word of wis-dom, A
de - liv - 'rance From chains of guilt and sin; I sought for peace and par - don, For

no - ble work to try, To give my life ful - fill - ment, My dreams to sat - is - fy.
true au - thor - i - ty, I sought to know life's pur - pose, To solve its mys - ter - y.
freedom from my fears, I sought a hope to cling to Be-yond these pass-ing years.

Refrain

I found them all in Je-sus, The Life, the Truth, the Way; Be - neath His flag

CODA *optional*

I'll take my stand And fol-low Him to - day. I'll fol-low Him to - day!

126   Give of Your Best to the Master

Howard B. Grose

Mrs. Charles Bennard

1. Give of your best to the Mas-ter; Give of the strength of your youth;
2. Give of your best to the Mas-ter; Give Him first place in your heart;
3. Give of your best to the Mas-ter; Naught else is wor-thy His love;

Throw your soul's fresh, glow-ing ar - dor In - to the bat-tle for truth.
Give Him first place in your serv - ice, Con - se-crate ev - ery part.
He gave Him-self for your ran - som, Gave up His glo-ry a - bove:

Je - sus has set the ex - am - ple; Daunt-less was He, young and brave;
Give, and to you shall be giv - en; God His be - lov - ed Son gave;
Laid down His life with-out mur - mur, You from sin's ru - in to save;

rall.

Give Him your loy - al de - vo - tion, Give Him the best that you have.
Grate-ful - ly seek-ing to serve Him, Give Him the best that you have.
Give Him your heart's ad - o - ra - tion, Give Him the best that you have.

Refrain

Give of your best to the Mas - ter; Give of the strength of your youth;

Clad in sal-va-tion's full ar-mor, Join in the bat-tle for truth.

God of Our Fathers

127

Daniel C. Roberts

George W. Warren

Trumpets, before each verse

1. God of our fa-thers, whose al-might-y hand
2. Thy love di-vine hath led us in the past,
3. From war's a-larms, from dead-ly pes-ti-lence,
4. Re-fresh Thy peo-ple on their toil-some way,

Leads forth in beau-ty all the star-ry band Of shin-ing worlds in
In this free land by Thee our lot is cast; Be Thou our rul-er,
Be Thy strong arm our ev-er-sure de-fense; Thy true re-li-gion
Lead us from night to nev-er-end-ing day; Fill all our lives with

splen-dor thru the skies, Our grate-ful songs be-fore Thy throne a-rise.
guard-ian, guide, and stay, Thy word our law, Thy paths our cho-sen way.
in our hearts in-crease, Thy boun-teous good-ness nour-ish us in peace.
love and grace di-vine, And glo-ry, laud, and praise be ev-er Thine!

128 Follow On

W. O. Cushing   *Robert Lowry*

1. Down in the val-ley with my Sav-iour I would go, Where the flow'rs are
2. Down in the val-ley with my Sav-iour I would go, Where the storms are
3. Down in the val-ley, or up-on the moun-tain steep, Close be-side my

bloom-ing and the sweet wa-ters flow. Ev-'ry-where He leads me I would
sweep-ing and the dark wa-ters flow. With His hand to lead me I will
Sav-iour would my soul ev-er keep. He will lead me safe-ly in the

fol-low, fol-low on, Walk-ing in His foot-steps till the crown be won.
nev-er, nev-er fear; Dan-ger can-not fright me if my Lord is near.
path that He has trod, Up to where they gath-er on the hills of God.

Refrain

Fol-low! fol-low! I will fol-low Je-sus! An-y-where, ev-'ry-where, I will fol-low on!

Fol-low! fol-low! I will fol-low Je-sus! Ev-'ry-where He leads me I will fol-low on!

I Would Be True

129

Howard A. Walter

Joseph Y. Peek

1. I would be true, for there are those who trust me; I would be
2. I would be friend of all— the foe, the friend - less; I would be
3. I would be prayer - ful thro' each bus - y mo - ment; I would be

pure, for there are those who care; I would be strong, for
giv - ing, and for - get the gift; I would be hum - ble,
con - stant - ly in touch with God; I would be tuned to

there is much to suf - fer; I would be brave, for there is
for I know my weak - ness; I would look up, and laugh, and
hear the slight - est whis - per; I would have faith to keep the

much to dare, I would be brave, for there is much to dare.
love, and lift, I would look up, and laugh, and love, and lift.
path Christ trod, I would have faith to keep the path Christ trod.

130

I'm a Soldier

John W. Peterson   *John W. Peterson*

1. A sol-dier in the ar-my of the King of kings am I, He called me to His
2. The bat-tle fierce is rag-ing o-ver land and o-ver sea, Wher-ev-er men have
3. Some day the bat-tle will be o-ver, vic-to-ry will come I won-der if I'll

col-ors and for Him I'll live or die; I'll go wher-e'er He bids me and I'll
borne the news of Christ and Cal-va-ry; The fight for souls must not be lost I
share the full re-ward a-wait-ing some; Will I have bat-tle scars to show in

do His least command, Be-neath the ban-ner of the cross I glad-ly take my stand
can-not fal-ter, no! But in the strength of Christ my Lord I'll on-ly for-ward go.
heav-en when we meet? How man-y crowns and tro-phies will I cast at Je-sus' feet?

Chorus

I'm a sol-dier in the ar-my, And the call to bat-tle loud-ly rings;

I'm a sol-dier in the ar-my, In the ar-my of the King of kings.

Am I a Soldier of the Cross? 131

Isaac Watts

Thomas A. Arne

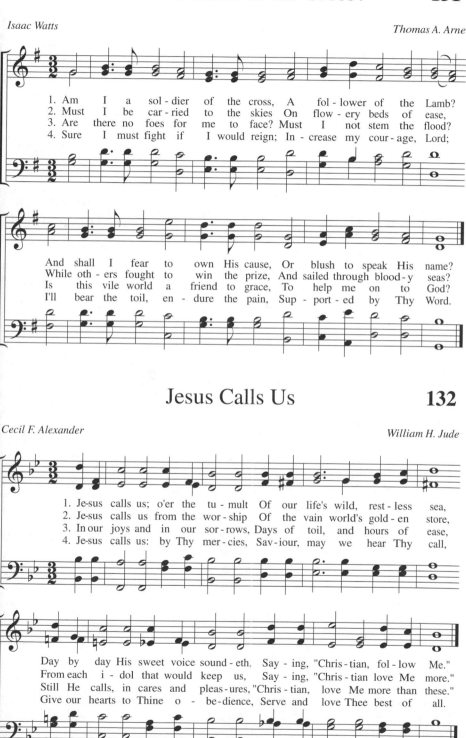

1. Am I a sol - dier of the cross, A fol - lower of the Lamb?
2. Must I be car - ried to the skies On flow - ery beds of ease,
3. Are there no foes for me to face? Must I not stem the flood?
4. Sure I must fight if I would reign; In - crease my cour - age, Lord;

And shall I fear to own His cause, Or blush to speak His name?
While oth - ers fought to win the prize, And sailed through blood - y seas?
Is this vile world a friend to grace, To help me on to God?
I'll bear the toil, en - dure the pain, Sup - port - ed by Thy Word.

Jesus Calls Us 132

Cecil F. Alexander

William H. Jude

1. Je-sus calls us; o'er the tu - mult Of our life's wild, rest - less sea,
2. Je-sus calls us from the wor - ship Of the vain world's gold - en store,
3. In our joys and in our sor - rows, Days of toil, and hours of ease,
4. Je-sus calls us: by Thy mer - cies, Sav-iour, may we hear Thy call,

Day by day His sweet voice sound - eth, Say - ing, "Chris - tian, fol - low Me."
From each i - dol that would keep us, Say - ing, "Chris - tian love Me more."
Still He calls, in cares and pleas - ures, "Chris - tian, love Me more than these."
Give our hearts to Thine o - be-dience, Serve and love Thee best of all.

133   Lead on, O King Eternal

Ernest W. Shurtleff   *Henry Smart*

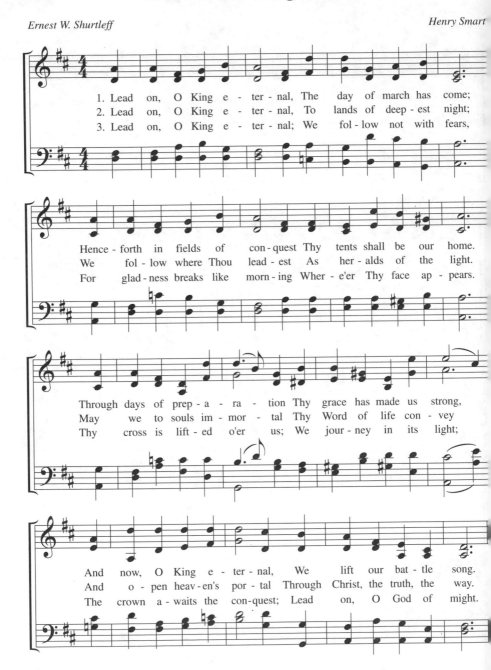

1. Lead on, O King e-ter-nal, The day of march has come;
2. Lead on, O King e-ter-nal, To lands of deep-est night;
3. Lead on, O King e-ter-nal; We fol-low not with fears,

Hence-forth in fields of con-quest Thy tents shall be our home.
We fol-low where Thou lead-est As her-alds of the light.
For glad-ness breaks like morn-ing Wher-e'er Thy face ap-pears.

Through days of prep-a-ra-tion Thy grace has made us strong,
May we to souls im-mor-tal Thy Word of life con-vey
Thy cross is lift-ed o'er us; We jour-ney in its light;

And now, O King e-ter-nal, We lift our bat-tle song.
And o-pen heav-en's por-tal Through Christ, the truth, the way.
The crown a-waits the con-quest; Lead on, O God of might.

O Zion Haste

Mary A. Thomson   *James Walch*

1. O   Zi - on, haste, thy mis - sion high   ful - fill - ing,   To   tell   to   all
2. Be - hold how man - y thou - sands still   are   ly - ing, Bound   in   the dark -
3. Pro - claim to   ev - ery peo - ple, tongue, and   na - tion, That   God,   in Whom
4. Give of   thy sons to bear the mes - sage glo - rious; Give   of   thy wealth
5. He comes a - gain: O   Zi - on,   ere   thou meet Him, Make known to   ev -

the   world that God is Light; That He who made all   na - tions is   not will-
some pris - on - house of   sin, With none to   tell them of   the Sav - iour's dy -
they live and move, is Love: Tell how He stooped to   save His lost cre - a -
to   speed them on their way; Pour out thy soul for them in prayer vic - to -
ery   heart His sav - ing grace; Let none whom He hath ran - somed fail to greet

Refrain

ing   One soul should per - ish, lost   in shades of night.
ing,   Or   of the   life He died for them to win.
tion,   And died on earth that man might live a - bove.   Pub - lish glad ti - dings,
rious; And all thou spend - est Je - sus   will re - pay.
Him, Through thy ne - glect, un - fit   to   see His face.

ti - dings of   peace,   Ti - dings of   Je - sus, re - demp - tion and re - lease.

135 Rescue the Perishing

Fanny J. Crosby

William H. Doane

1. Res - cue the per - ish - ing, Care for the dy - ing,
2. Though they are slight - ing Him, Still He is wait - ing,
3. Down in the hu - man heart, Crushed by the tempt - er,
4. Res - cue the per - ish - ing, Du - ty de - mands it;

Snatch them in pit - y from sin and the grave;
Wait - ing the pen - i - tent child to re - ceive;
Feel - ings lie bur - ied that grace can re - store;
Strength for thy la - bor the Lord will pro - vide.

Weep o'er the err - ing one, Lift up the fall - en,
Plead with them ear - nest - ly, Plead with them gen - tly,
Touched by a lov - ing heart, Wak - ened by kind - ness,
Back to the nar - row way Pa - tient - ly win them;

Tell them of Je - sus the might - y to save.
He will for - give if they on - ly be - lieve.
Chords that were bro - ken will vi - brate once more.
Tell the poor wan - derer a Sav - iour has died.

Refrain

Res - cue the per - ish - ing, Care for the dy - ing;

Je - sus is mer - ci - ful, Je - sus will save.

Where He Leads Me 136

E. W. Blandy *J. S. Norris*

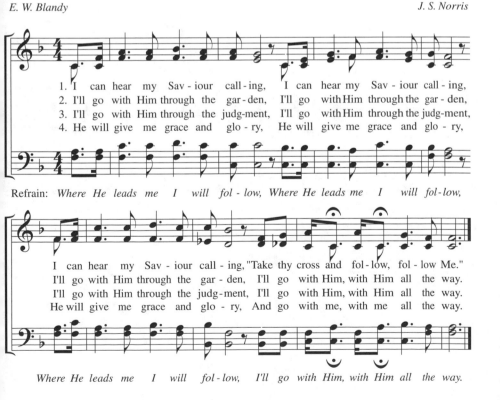

1. I can hear my Sav - iour call - ing, I can hear my Sav - iour call - ing,
2. I'll go with Him through the gar - den, I'll go with Him through the gar - den,
3. I'll go with Him through the judg - ment, I'll go with Him through the judg - ment,
4. He will give me grace and glo - ry, He will give me grace and glo - ry,

Refrain: *Where He leads me I will fol - low, Where He leads me I will fol - low,*

I can hear my Sav - iour call - ing, "Take thy cross and fol - low, fol - low Me."
I'll go with Him through the gar - den, I'll go with Him, with Him all the way.
I'll go with Him through the judg - ment, I'll go with Him, with Him all the way.
He will give me grace and glo - ry, And go with me, with me all the way.

Where He leads me I will fol - low, I'll go with Him, with Him all the way.

Soldiers of Christ, Arise

Charles Wesley   *George J. Elvey*

1. Sol - diers of Christ, a - rise, And put your ar - mor on,
2. Stand, then, in His great might, With all His strength en - dued;
3. Leave no un - guard - ed place, No weak - ness of the soul,

Strong in the strength which God sup - plies Through His e - ter - nal Son,
And take, to arm you for the fight, The pan - o - ply of God!
Take ev - ery vir - tue, ev - ery grace, And for - ti - fy the whole.

Strong in the Lord of Hosts, And in His might - y power,
That, hav - ing all things done, And all your con - flicts past,
From strength to strength go on; Wres - tle, and fight, and pray;

Who in the strength of Je - sus trusts Is more than con - quer - or.
Ye may o'er - come, thro' Christ a - lone, And stand en - tire at last.
Tread all the powers of dark - ness down, And win the well - fought day!

Stand Up for Jesus

George Duffield   *George J. Webb*

1. Stand up, stand up for Je - sus, Ye sol - diers of the cross,
2. Stand up, stand up for Je - sus, The trump - et call o - bey;
3. Stand up, stand up for Je - sus, Stand in His strength a - lone;
4. Stand up, stand up for Je - sus, The strife will not be long;

Lift high His roy - al ban - ner, It must not suf - fer loss;
Forth to the might - y con - flict, In this His glor - ious day.
The arm of flesh will fail you— Ye dare not trust your own;
This day the noise of bat - tle, The next, the vic - tor's song;

From vic - tory un - to vic - tory, His ar - my shall He lead,
"Ye that are men, now serve Him," A - gainst un - num - bered foes;
Put on the gos - pel ar - mor, Each piece put on with prayer;
To him that o - ver - com - eth, A crown of life shall be;

Till ev - ery foe is van - quished And Christ is Lord in - deed.
Let cour - age rise with dan - ger, And strength to strength op - pose.
Where du - ty calls, or dan - ger, Be nev - er want - ing there.
He with the King of glo - ry Shall reign e - ter - nal - ly.

139 Take Time to Be Holy

William D. Longstaff *George C. Stebbins*

1. Take time to be ho - ly— Speak oft with thy Lord;
2. Take time to be ho - ly— The world rush - es on;
3. Take time to be ho - ly— Let Him be thy guide,
4. Take time to be ho - ly— Be calm in thy soul,

A - bide in Him al - ways, And feed on His Word.
Spend much time in se - cret With Je - sus a - lone.
And run not be - fore Him What - ev - er be - tide.
Each thought and each mo - tive Be - neath His con - trol.

Make friends of God's chil - dren; Help those who are weak,
By look - ing to Je - sus, Like Him thou shalt be;
In joy or in sor - row, Still fol - low thy Lord;
Thus, led by His Spir - it To foun - tains of love,

For - get - ting in noth - ing His bless - ing to seek.
Thy friends in thy con - duct His like - ness shall see.
And, look - ing to Je - sus, Still trust in His Word.
Thou soon shalt be fit - ted For serv - ice a - bove.

Trust and Obey

140

John H. Sammis

Daniel B. Towner

1. When we walk with the Lord In the light of His word, What a glo-ry He
2. Not a shad-ow can rise, Not a cloud in the skies, But His smile quick-ly
3. But we nev-er can prove The de-lights of His love Un-til all on the
4. Then in fel-low-ship sweet We will sit at His feet, Or we'll walk by His

sheds on our way! While we do His good will, He a-bides with us still
drives it a-way; Not a doubt nor a fear, Not a sigh nor a tear
al-ter we lay; For the fa-vor He shows And the joy He be-stows
side in the way; What He says we will do, Where He sends we will go—

Refrain

And with all who will trust and o-bey.
Can a-bide while we trust and o-bey.
Are for them who will trust and o-bey.
Nev-er fear, on-ly trust and o-bey.

Trust and o-bey, for there's

no oth-er way To be hap-py in Je-sus, But to trust and o-bey.

141   We've a Story to Tell to the Nations

H. Ernest Nichol   *H. Ernest Nichol*

1. We've a sto - ry to tell to the na - tions That shall turn their
2. We've a song to be sung to the na - tions That shall lift their
3. We've a mes - sage to give to the na - tions— That the Lord who
4. We've a Sav - ior to show to the na - tions Who the path of

hearts to the right, A stor - ry of truth and mer - cy, A
hearts to the Lord, A song that shall con - quer e - vil And
reign - eth a - bove Hath sent us His Son to save us And
sor - row hath trod, That all of the world's great peo - ples Might

sto - ry of peace and light, A sto - ry of peace and light.
shat - ter the spear and sword, And shat - ter the spear and sword.
show us that God is love, And show us that God is love.
come to the truth of God, Might come to the truth of God.

Chorus

For the dark-ness shall turn to dawn-ing, And the dawn-ing to noon-day bright,

And Christ's great king-dom shall come to earth, The king-dom of love and light.

Wherever He Leads I'll Go 142

B. B. McKinney   *B. B. McKinney*

1. "Take up thy cross and fol-low Me," I heard my Mas-ter say;
2. He drew me clos-er to His side, I sought His will to know,
3. It may be through the shad-ows dim, Or o'er the storm-y sea,
4. My heart, my life, my all I bring To Christ who loves me so;

"I gave My life to ran-som thee, Sur-ren-der your all to-day."
And in that will I now a-bide, Where-ev-er He leads I'll go.
I take my cross and fol-low Him, Where-ev-er He lead-eth me.
He is my Mas-ter, Lord, and King, Wher-ev-er He leads I'll go.

Refrain

Where-ev-er He leads I'll go, Where-ev-er He leads I'll go,

I'll fol-low my Christ who loves me so, Wher-ev-er He leads I'll go.

143   Who Is on the Lord's Side?

Frances Ridley Havergal

German Melody
Arr. by John Goss

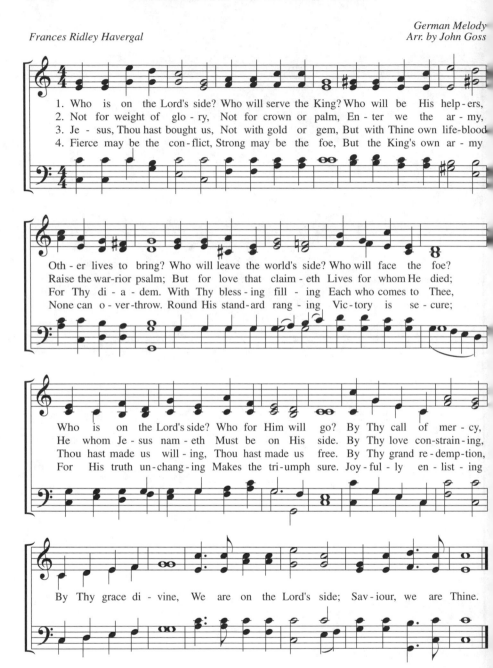

1. Who is on the Lord's side? Who will serve the King? Who will be His help-ers,
2. Not for weight of glo - ry, Not for crown or palm, En - ter we the ar - my,
3. Je - sus, Thou hast bought us, Not with gold or gem, But with Thine own life-blood
4. Fierce may be the con-flict, Strong may be the foe, But the King's own ar - my

Oth - er lives to bring? Who will leave the world's side? Who will face the foe?
Raise the war-rior psalm; But for love that claim - eth Lives for whom He died;
For Thy di - a - dem. With Thy bless-ing fill - ing Each who comes to Thee,
None can o - ver-throw. Round His stand-ard rang - ing Vic-tory is se - cure;

Who is on the Lord's side? Who for Him will go? By Thy call of mer - cy,
He whom Je - sus nam - eth Must be on His side. By Thy love con-strain-ing,
Thou hast made us will - ing, Thou hast made us free. By Thy grand re - demp-tion,
For His truth un-chang-ing Makes the tri-umph sure. Joy - ful - ly en - list - ing

By Thy grace di - vine, We are on the Lord's side; Sav - iour, we are Thine.

Yield Not to Temptation

144

Horatio R. Palmer   *Horatio R. Palmer*

1. Yield not to temp - ta - tion, For yield - ing is sin— Each vic - tory will
2. Shun e - vil com - pan - ions, Bad lan - guage dis - dain, God's name hold in
3. To him that o'er - com - eth God giv - eth a crown; Through faith we shall

help you Some oth - er to win; Fight man - ful - ly on - ward,
rev - erence, Nor take it in vain; Be thought-ful and ear - nest,
con - quer Though of - ten cast down; He, who is our Sav - ior,

Dark pas-sions sub - due; Look ev-er to Je - sus, He will car-ry you through.
Kind - heart-ed and true; Look ev-er to Je - sus, He will car-ry you through.
Our strength will re - new; Look ev-er to Je - sus, He will car-ry you through.

Refrain

Ask the Sav - ior to help you, Com - fort, strength-en, and keep you;

He is will - ing to aid you, He will car - ry you through.

145 All the Way My Savior Leads Me

Fanny J. Crosby   Robert Lowry

1. All the way my Sav-ior leads me— What have I to ask be-side?
2. All the way my Sav-ior leads me— Cheers each wind-ing path I tread,
3. All the way my Sav-ior leads me— O the full-ness of His love!

Can I doubt His ten-der mer-cy, Who thru life has been my Guide?
Gives me grace for ev-'ry tri - al, Feeds me with the liv - ing bread.
Per - fect rest to me is prom-ised In my Fa - ther's house a - bove.

Heav'n-ly peace, di - vin - est com-fort, Here by faith in Him to dwell!
Tho my wea - ry steps may fal - ter And my soul a - thirst may be,
When my spir - it, clothed im - mor-tal, Wings its flight to realms of day,

For I know, what - e'er be - fall me, Je-sus do - eth all things well; well.
Gush-ing from the Rock be - fore me, Lo! a spring of joy I see; see.
This my song thru end-less a - ges: Je-sus led me all the way; way.

Anywhere with Jesus

Jessie B. Pounds

Daniel B. Towner

1. An - y - where with Je-sus I can safe - ly go; An - y - where He
2. An - y - where with Je-sus I need fear no ill, Though temp - ta - tions
3. An - y - where with Je-sus I am not a - lone; Oth - er friends may
4. An - y - where with Je-sus o - ver land and sea, Tell - ing souls in
5. An - y - where with Je-sus I can go to sleep, When the dark - ening

leads me in this world be - low; An - y - where with - out Him dear-est
gath - er round my path-way still; He Him-self was tempt - ed that He
fail me, He is still my own; Though His hand may lead me o - ver
dark - ness of sal - va - tion free; Read - y as He sum-mons me to
shad-ows round a - bout me creep; Know-ing I shall wak - en, nev - er

joys would fade; An - y - where with Je-sus I am not a - fraid.
might help me; An - y - where with Je-sus I may vic - tor be.
drear - y ways; An - y - where with Je-sus is a house of praise.
go or stay, An - y - where with Je-sus when He points the way.
more to roam, An - y - where with Je-sus will be home, sweet home.

Refrain

An - y - where! An - y - where! Fear I can - not know;

An - y - where with Je - sus I can safe - ly go.

147 Bringing in the Sheaves

Knowles Shaw

George A. Minor

1. Sow-ing in the morn-ing, sow-ing seeds of kind-ness, Sow-ing in the
2. Sow-ing in the sun-shine, sow-ing in the shad-ows; Fear-ing nei-ther
3. Go-ing forth with weep-ing, sow-ing for the Mas-ter, Tho' the loss sus-

noon-tide and the dew-y eve; Wait-ing for the har-vest, and the
clouds nor win-ter's chill-ing breeze; By and by the har-vest and the
tained our spir-it of-ten grieves; When our weep-ing's o-ver, He will

time of reap-ing, We shall come re-joic-ing, bring-ing in the sheaves.
la-bor end-ed, We shall come re-joic-ing, bring-ing in the sheaves.
bid us wel-come, We shall come re-joic-ing, bring-ing in the sheaves.

Refrain

Bring-ing in the sheaves, bring-ing in the sheaves, We shall come re-
Bring-ing in the sheaves, bring-ing in the sheaves, We shall come re-

1. joic-ing, bring-ing in the sheaves;
2. joic-ing, bring-ing in the sheaves.

Christ Receiveth Sinful Men

Erdmann Neumeister
Trans. by Emma F. Bevan

James McGranahan

1. Sin - ners Je - sus will re - ceive; Sound this word of grace to all
2. Come, and He will give you rest; Trust Him, for His word is plain;
3. Now my heart con - demns me not; Pure be - fore the law I stand;
4. Christ re - ceiv - eth sin - ful men, E - ven me with all my sin;

Who the heaven - ly path - way leave, All who lin - ger, all who fall.
He will take the sin - ful - est; Christ re - ceiv - eth sin - ful men.
He who cleansed me from all spot Sat - is - fied its last de - mand.
Purged from ev - ery spot and stain, Heaven with Him I en - ter in.

Refrain

Sing it o'er and o'er a - gain; Christ re -
Sing it o'er a-gain, sing it o'er a-gain; Christ re -

ceiv - eth sin - ful men; Make the mes - sage
ceiv-eth sin-ful men, Christ re-ceiv-eth sin-ful men; Make the mes-sage plain,

clear and plain: Christ re - ceiv - eth sin - ful men.
make the mes - sage plain:

149   I Love to Tell the Story

Catherine Hankey

William G. Fischer

1. I love to tell the sto - ry Of un - seen things a - bove, Of
2. I love to tell the sto - ry, More won - der - ful it seems Than
3. I love to tell the sto - ry, 'Tis pleas - ant to re - peat What
4. I love to tell the sto - ry, For those who know it best Seem

Je - sus and His glo - ry, Of Je - sus and His love. I love to
all the gold - en fan - cies Of all our gold - en dreams. I love to
seems, each time I tell it, More won - der - ful - ly sweet. I love to
hun - ger - ing and thirst - ing To hear it like the rest. And when, in

tell the sto - ry, Be - cause I know 'tis true; It sat - is - fies my
tell the sto - ry, It did so much for me; And that is just the
tell the sto - ry, For some have nev - er heard The mes - sage of sal -
scenes of glo - ry, I sing the new, new song, 'Twill be the old, old

Refrain

long - ings As noth - ing else can do.
rea - son I tell it now to thee.
va - tion From God's own ho - ly word.
sto - ry That I have loved so long.

I love to tell the sto - ry, 'Twill

be my theme in glo - ry To tell the old, old sto - ry Of Je - sus and His love.

In My Heart There Rings a Melody   150

Elton M. Roth   *Elton M. Roth*

1. I have a song that Je - sus gave me, It was sent from
2. I love the Christ who died on Cal - v'ry, For He washed my
3. 'Twill be my end - less theme in glo - ry, With the an - gels

heav'n a - bove; There nev - er was a sweet - er mel - o - dy, 'Tis a
sins a - way; He put with - in my heart a mel - o - dy, And I
I will sing; 'Twill be a song with glo - rious har - mo - ny, When the

Chorus

mel - o - dy of love.   In my heart there rings a mel - o - dy,
know it's here to stay.
courts of heav - en ring.

There rings a mel - o - dy with heav - en's har - mo - ny;   In my

heart there rings a mel - o - dy; There rings a mel - o - dy of love.

151   It's Just Like His Great Love

Edna R. Worrell

DeKoven

1. A Friend I have, called Je - sus, Whose love is strong and true, And nev-
2. Some-times the clouds of trou - ble Be - dim the sky a - bove, I can-
3. When sor - row's clouds o'er - take me, And break up - on my head, When life
4. Oh, I could sing for - ev - er Of Je - sus' love di - vine, Of all

er fails how - e'er 'tis tried, No mat - ter what I do; I've sinned a-
not see my Sav - ior's face, I doubt His won - drous love; But He, from
seems worse than use - less, And I were bet - ter dead; I take my
His care and ten - der - ness For this poor life of mine; His love is

gainst this love of His, But when I knelt to pray, Con - fess - ing all my
Heav - en's mer - cy - seat, Be - hold - ing my de - spair, In pit - y bursts the
grief to Je - sus then, Nor do I go in vain, For heav'n - ly hope He
in and o - ver all, And wind and waves o - bey When Je - sus whis - pers

guilt to Him, The sin - clouds rolled a - way.
clouds be - tween, And shows me He is there.
gives that cheers Like sun - shine aft - er rain.   It's just like Je - sus to
"Peace, be still!" And rolls the clouds a - way.

Chorus

It's just like Je - sus to roll the clouds a - way, It's just like Je - sus to keep me day by day,

It's just like Je-sus all a-long the way, It's just like His great love.

Jesus Saves

152

Priscilla J. Owens

William J. Kirkpatrick

1. We have heard the joy-ful sound: Je-sus saves! Je-sus saves! Spread the ti-dings
2. Waft it on the roll-ing tide: Je-sus saves! Je-sus saves! Tell to sin-ners
3. Sing a-bove the bat-tle strife: Je-sus saves! Je-sus saves! By His death and
4. Give the winds a might-y voice: Je-sus saves! Je-sus saves! Let the na-tions

all a-round: Je-sus saves! Je-sus saves! Bear the news to ev-ery land, Climb the
far and wide: Je-sus saves! Je-sus saves! Sing, ye is-lands of the sea; Ech-o
end-less life, Je-sus saves! Je-sus saves! Sing it soft-ly through the gloom, When the
now re-joice, Je-sus saves! Je-sus saves! Shout sal-va-tion full and free; High-est

steeps and cross the waves; On-ward! 'tis our Lord's com-mand; Je-sus saves! Je-sus saves!
back, ye o-cean caves; Earth shall keep her ju-bi-lee: Je-sus saves! Je-sus saves!
heart for mer-cy craves; Sing in tri-umph o'er the tomb, Je-sus saves! Je-sus saves!
hills and deep-est caves; This our song of vic-to-ry: Je-sus saves! Je-sus saves!

153 My Redeemer

Philip P. Bliss   *James McGranahan*

1. I will sing of my Re-deem-er, And His won-drous love to me;
2. I will tell the won-drous sto-ry, How my lost es-tate to save,
3. I will praise my dear Re-deem-er, His tri-um-phant power I'll tell,
4. I will sing of my Re-deem-er, And His heaven-ly love to me;

On the cru-el cross He suf-fered, From the curse to set me free.
In His bound-less love and mer-cy, He the ran-som free-ly gave.
How the vic-to-ry He giv-eth O-ver sin, and death, and hell.
He from death to life hath brought me, Son of God, with Him to be.

Chorus

Sing, oh, sing of my Re-deem-er,
of my Re-deem-er, Sing, oh, sing of my Re-deem-er,

With His blood He pur-chased me,
He pur-chased me, With His blood He pur-chased me,

On the cross He sealed my par-don,
He sealed my par-don, On the cross He sealed my par-don,

Paid the debt, and made me free.
and made me free, and made me free.

Revive Us Again

154

William P. Mackay

John J. Husband

1. We praise Thee, O God, for the Son of Thy love, For Je - sus Who
2. We praise Thee, O God, for Thy Spir - it of light, Who has shown us our
3. All glo - ry and praise to the Lamb that was slain, Who has borne all our
4. Re - vive us a - gain, fill each heart with Thy love; May each soul be re -

Refrain

died and is now gone a - bove.
Sav - iour and scat - tered our night.
sins and has cleansed ev - ery stain.
kin - dled with fire from a - bove.

Hal - le - lu - jah! Thine the glo - ry, Hal - le -

lu - jah! A - men; Hal - le - lu - jah! Thine the glo - ry; Re - vive us a - gain.

155 My Savior's Love

Charles H. Gabriel   *Charles H. Gabriel*

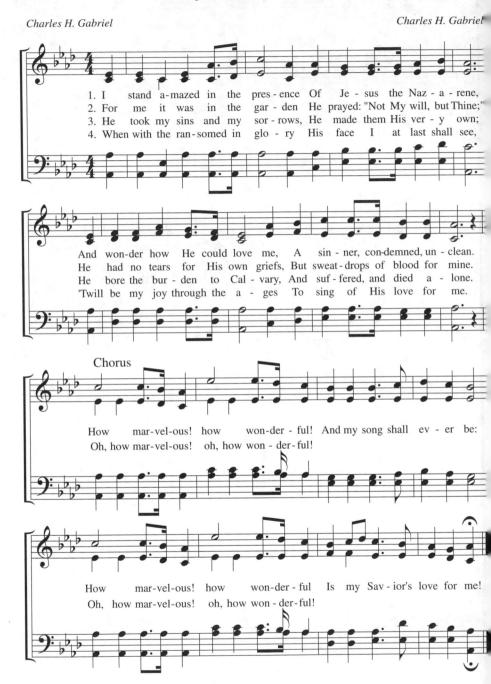

1. I stand a-mazed in the pres - ence Of Je - sus the Naz - a - rene,
2. For me it was in the gar - den He prayed: "Not My will, but Thine;"
3. He took my sins and my sor - rows, He made them His ver - y own;
4. When with the ran-somed in glo - ry His face I at last shall see,

And won-der how He could love me, A sin - ner, con-demned, un - clean.
He had no tears for His own griefs, But sweat-drops of blood for mine.
He bore the bur - den to Cal - vary, And suf - fered, and died a - lone.
'Twill be my joy through the a - ges To sing of His love for me.

Chorus

How mar-vel-ous! how won-der - ful! And my song shall ev - er be:
Oh, how mar-vel-ous! oh, how won - der-ful!

How mar-vel-ous! how won-der - ful Is my Sav - ior's love for me!
Oh, how mar-vel-ous! oh, how won - der-ful!

Isn't the Love of Jesus Something Wonderful!

156

John W. Peterson

John W. Peterson

1. There will nev-er be a sweet-er sto-ry, Sto-ry of the Sav-ior's
2. Bound-less as the u-ni-verse a-round me, Reach-ing to the far-thest
3. Love be-yond our hu-man com-pre-hend-ing, Love of God in Christ how

love di-vine, Love that bro't Him from the realms of glo-ry
soul a-way, Sav-ing, keep-ing love it was that found me,
can it be? This will be my theme and nev-er end-ing,

Chorus

Just to save a sin-ful soul like mine. Is-n't the love of Je-sus
That is why my heart can tru-ly say:
Great re-deem-ing love of Cal-va-ry.

some-thing won-der-ful, won-der-ful, it is won-der-ful; O is-n't the love of

Je-sus some-thing won-der-ful! Won-der-ful it is to me.
to me.

157   O It Is Wonderful to Be a Christian

John W. Peterson   *John W. Peterson*

1. Life has pur - pose now it nev - er had be - fore. There is
2. I can go di - rect - ly to the Lord in prayer. He has
3. And the hope of heav - en's glo - ries thrills me so. Where I'll

mean - ing to each day and e - ven more; For a joy and peace I
told me I may bold - ly en - ter there, And He lis - tens as His
live with Christ for - ev - er - more, I know. That is why the things of

can't ex - plain is mine, Since I found new life in Christ, my Lord di - vine.
prom - is - es I plead. I find mer - cy there and grace for ev - 'ry need.
earth I loose - ly hold; I've e - ter - nal rich - es, bet - ter far than gold.

Chorus

O it is won - der - ful to be a Chris - tian; O it is won - der - ful to

be God's child! O it is won-der-ful to have your sins for-giv-en;

O it is won-der-ful to be re-deemed, jus - ti-fied, for-ev - er rec - on-ciled!

There's a Wideness in God's Mercy   158

Frederick W. Faber

Lizzie S. Tourjee

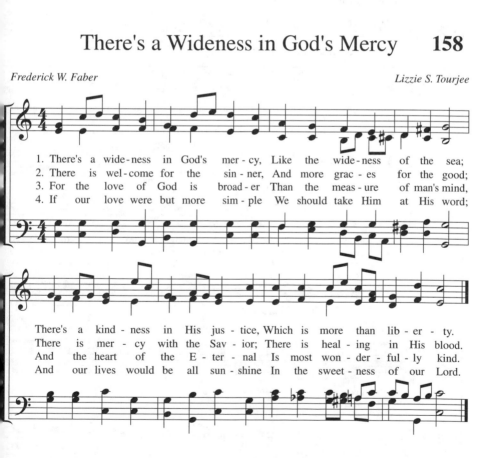

1. There's a wide-ness in God's mer - cy, Like the wide-ness of the sea;
2. There is wel-come for the sin - ner, And more grac - es for the good;
3. For the love of God is broad - er Than the meas - ure of man's mind,
4. If our love were but more sim - ple We should take Him at His word;

There's a kind - ness in His jus - tice, Which is more than lib - er - ty.
There is mer - cy with the Sav - ior; There is heal - ing in His blood.
And the heart of the E - ter - nal Is most won - der - ful - ly kind.
And our lives would be all sun - shine In the sweet - ness of our Lord.

159 Praise Him! Praise Him!

Fanny J. Crosby

Chester G. Aller

1. Praise Him! praise Him! Je - sus, our bless - ed Re - deem - er! Sing, O
2. Praise Him! praise Him! Je - sus, our bless - ed Re - deem - er! For our
3. Praise Him! praise Him! Je - sus, our bless - ed Re - deem - er! Heav'n - ly

earth— His won - der - ful love pro - claim! Hail Him! hail Him! high-est arch
sins He suf - fered and bled and died; He our Rock, our hope of e -
por - tals loud with ho - san - nas ring! Je - sus, Sav - ior, reigneth for

an-gels in glo - ry, Strength and hon - or give to His ho - ly name!
ter-nal sal - va - tion, Hail Him! hail Him! Je - sus the Cru - ci - fied.
ev - er and ev - er, Crown Him! crown Him! Proph - et and Priest and King!

Like a shep - herd Je - sus will guard His chil-dren— In His arms He
Sound His prais - es— Je - sus who bore our sor-rows—Love un - bound-ed,
Christ is com - ing, o - ver the world vic - to - rious—Pow'r and glo - ry

Refrain

car - ries them all day long: Praise Him! praise Him! tell of His
won - der - ful, deep and strong:
un - to the Lord be - long:

ex - cel - lent great - ness! Praise Him! praise him! ev - er in joy - ful song!

Redeemed

160

Fanny J. Crosby

William J. Kirkpatrick

1. Re-deemed—how I love to pro-claim it! Re-deemed by the blood of the Lamb;
2. Re-deemed and so hap-py in Je-sus; No lan-guage my rap-ture can tell.
3. I think of my bless-ed Re-deem-er, I think of Him all the day long;
4. I know I shall see in His beau-ty The King in whose law I de-light,

Re-deemed through His in-fi-nite mer-cy, His child, and for-ev-er, I am.
I know that the light of His pres-ence With me doth con-tin-ual-ly dwell.
I sing, for I can-not be si-lent; His love is the theme of my song.
Who lov-ing-ly guard-eth my foot-steps And giv-eth me songs in the night.

Refrain

Re - deemed, re - deemed, Re-deemed by the blood of the Lamb;
re-deemed, re-deemed,

Re - deemed, re - deemed, His child, and for-ev-er, I am.
re-deemed, re-deemed,

161   O How I Love Jesus

Frederick Whitfield

Early American Melody

1. There is a name I love to hear, I love to sing its worth;
2. It tells me of a Sav-ior's love, Who died to set me free;
3. It tells me what my Fa-ther hath In store for ev-'ry day,
4. It tells of One whose lov-ing heart Can feel my deep-est woe,

It sounds like mu-sic in mine ear, The sweet-est name on earth.
It tells me of His pre-cious blood, The sin-ner's per-fect plea.
And, though I tread a dark-some path, Yields sun-shine all the way.
Who in each sor-row bears a part That none can bear be-low.

Chorus

O how I love Je-sus, O how I love Je-sus,

O how I love Je-sus— Be-cause He first loved me!

What a Wonderful Savior

Elisha A. Hoffman

Elisha A. Hoffman

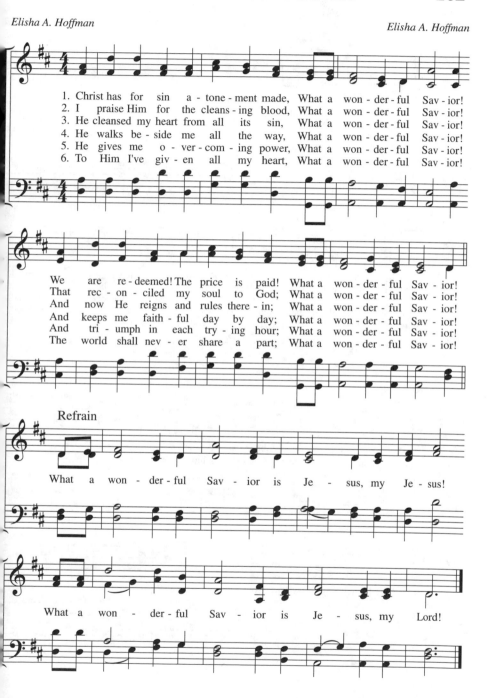

1. Christ has for sin a - tone - ment made, What a won - der - ful Sav - ior!
2. I praise Him for the cleans - ing blood, What a won - der - ful Sav - ior!
3. He cleansed my heart from all its sin, What a won - der - ful Sav - ior!
4. He walks be - side me all the way, What a won - der - ful Sav - ior!
5. He gives me o - ver - com - ing power, What a won - der - ful Sav - ior!
6. To Him I've giv - en all my heart, What a won - der - ful Sav - ior!

We are re - deemed! The price is paid! What a won - der - ful Sav - ior!
That rec - on - ciled my soul to God; What a won - der - ful Sav - ior!
And now He reigns and rules there - in; What a won - der - ful Sav - ior!
And keeps me faith - ful day by day; What a won - der - ful Sav - ior!
And tri - umph in each try - ing hour; What a won - der - ful Sav - ior!
The world shall nev - er share a part; What a won - der - ful Sav - ior!

Refrain

What a won - der - ful Sav - ior is Je - sus, my Je - sus!

What a won - der - ful Sav - ior is Je - sus, my Lord!

163 Since I Have Been Redeemed

Edwin O. Excell

Edwin O. Excell

1. I have a song I love to sing, Since I have been re-deemed,
2. I have a Christ that sat-is-fies, Since I have been re-deemed,
3. I have a wit-ness bright and clear, Since I have been re-deemed,
4. I have a joy I can't ex-press, Since I have been re-deemed,
5. I have a home pre-pared for me, Since I have been re-deemed,

Of my Re-deem-er, Sav-ior, King— Since I have been re-deemed.
To do His will my high-est prize— Since I have been re-deemed.
Dis-pell-ing ev-ery doubt and fear— Since I have been re-deemed.
All through His blood and right-eous-ness— Since I have been re-deemed.
Where I shall dwell e-ter-nal-ly— Since I have been re-deemed.

Refrain

Since I have been re-deemed, Since I have been re-
Since I have been re-deemed, since I have been re-deemed,

deemed, I will glo-ry in His name; Since I have
Since I have been re-deemed,

been re - deemed,   I will glo - ry in the Sav - ior's   name.
since   I have been re-deemed,

O Say, but I'm Glad

164

Rev. James P. Sullivan

Mildred Lacour Sullivan

1. There is a song in my heart to - day, Something I nev - er had;
2. Won - der - ful, mar - vel - ous love He brings, In - to a heart that's sad;
3. Won't you come to Him with all your care, Wea - ry and worn and sad?

Je - sus has tak - en my sins a - way, O say, but I'm glad!
Thru dark - est tun - nels the soul just sings, O say, but I'm glad!
You, too, will sing as His love you share, O say, but I'm glad!

Chorus

O say, but I'm glad, I'm glad, O say, but I'm glad!

Je-sus has come and my cup's o-ver-rur, O say, but I'm glad!

165 Sooner or Later

1. Soon-er or lat-er the skies will be bright, Tears will be all wiped a-way;
2. Soon-er or lat-er, our Lord knows the hour, He'll send His be-lov-ed Son;
3. Soon-er or lat-er, yes, soon-er for some, Dark-ness will all then be past;

Soon-er or lat-er, then com-eth the light, Night will be turned in-to day. (glad day.)
Soon-er or lat-er, in His might and pow'r, Our bat-tles all will be won. (be won.)
Soon-er or lat-er our Sav-iour will come, With Him your lot be cast? (be cast?)

Chorus

Soon-er or lat-er cares will have flown Sun-shine and glad-ness we'll see; (we'll see;) Soon-er or lat-er God call-eth His own, With Him for-ev-er to be. (to be.)

Beulah Land

Edgar Page Stites

John R. Sweeney

1. I've reached the land of corn and wine, And all its rich-es free-ly mine;
2. My Sav-ior comes and walks with me, And sweet com-mun-ion here have we;
3. A sweet per-fume up-on the breeze Is borne from ev-er-ver-nal trees
4. The zeph-yrs seem to float to me Sweet sounds of heav-en's mel-o-dy,

Here shines un-dimmed one bliss-ful day, For all my night has passed a-way.
He gen-tly leads me by His hand, For this is heav-en's bor-der-land.
And flow'rs that nev-er-fad-ing grow, Where streams of life for-ev-er flow.
As an-gels with the white-robed throng Join in the sweet Re-demp-tion song.

Chorus

O Beu-lah Land, sweet Beu-lah Land! As on thy high-est mount I stand,

I look a-way a-cross the sea, Where man-sions are pre-pared for me,

And view the shin-ing glo-ry-shore—My heav'n, my home for-ev-er-more!

167   Oh, That Will Be Glory

Charles H. Gabriel   *Charles H. Gabriel*

On Jordan's Stormy Banks

Samuel Stennett

Early American
Arr. by R. M. McIntosh

1. On Jor - dan's storm - y banks I stand, And cast a wish - ful eye
2. All o'er those wide - ex - tend - ed plains Shines one e - ter - nal day;
3. No chill - ing winds nor poi - s'nous breath Can reach that health - ful shore;
4. When shall I reach that hap - py place, And be for - ev - er blest?

To Ca - naan's fair and hap - py land, Where my pos - ses - sions lie.
There God the Son for - ev - er reigns And scat - ters night a - way.
Sick - ness and sor - row, pain and death Are felt and feared no more.
When shall I see my Fa - ther's face, And in His bos - om rest?

Refrain

I am bound for the prom - ised land, I am bound for the prom - ised land;

O who will come and go with me? I am bound for the prom - ised land.

169 Saved by Grace

Fanny J. Crosby

George C. Stebbins
Arr. by Norman Johnson

1. Some day the sil - ver cord will break, And I no more as now shall sing;
2. Some day my earth - ly house will fall, I can - not tell how soon 'twill be,
3. Some day, when fades the gold - en sun Be - neath the ro - sy - tint - ed west,
4. Some day; till then I'll watch and wait, My lamp all trimm'd and burn - ing bright,

But, O, the joy when I shall wake With - in the pal - ace of the King!
But this I know— my All in All Has now a place in Heav'n for me.
My bless - ed Lord shall say, "Well done!" And I shall en - ter in - to rest.
That when my Sav - iour ope's the gate, My soul to Him may take its flight.

Chorus

And I shall see Him face to face, And tell the sto - ry— Sav'd by grace;

And I shall see Him face to face, And tell the sto - ry— Sav'd by grace.

Shall We Gather at the River?   170

Robert Lowry   Robert Lowry

1. Shall we gath-er at the riv-er, Where bright an-gel feet have trod,
2. On the bos-om of the riv-er, Where the Sav-ior-King we own,
3. Ere we reach the shin-ing riv-er, Lay we ev-'ry bur-den down;
4. Soon we'll reach the shin-ing riv-er, Soon our pil-grim-age will cease;

With its crys-tal tide for-ev-er Flow-ing by the throne of God?
We shall meet and sor-row nev-er 'Neath the glo-ry of the throne.
Grace our spir-its will de-liv-er And pro-vide a robe and crown.
Soon our hap-py hearts will quiv-er With the mel-o-dy of peace.

Chorus

Yes, we'll gath-er at the riv-er, The beau-ti-ful, the beau-ti-ful riv-er,

Gath-er with the saints at the riv-er That flows by the throne of God.

171 Sweet By and By

Sanford F. Bennett   *Joseph P. Webster*

1. There's a land that is fair - er than day, And by faith we can
2. We shall sing on that beau - ti - ful shore The me - lo - di - ous
3. To our boun - ti - ful Fa - ther a - bove, We will of - fer our

see it a - far; For the Fa - ther waits o - ver the way, To pre-
songs of the blest, And our spir - its shall sor - row no more, Not a
trib - ute of praise, For the glo - ri - ous gift of His love, And the

Chorus

pare us a dwell - ing - place there.   In the sweet   by and
sigh for the bless - ing of rest.   In the sweet
bless - ings that hal - low our days.

by,   We shall meet on that beau - ti - ful shore; In the
by and by,   by and by,

sweet   by and by,   We shall meet on that beau - ti - ful shore.
In the sweet   by and by,

When We All Get to Heaven

Eliza E. Hewitt

Emily D. Wilson

172

1. Sing the won-drous love of Je - sus, Sing His mer - cy and His grace;
2. While we walk the pil - grim path-way Clouds will o - ver - spread the sky;
3. Let us then be true and faith-ful, Trust - ing, serv-ing ev - 'ry day;
4. On - ward to the prize be - fore us! Soon His beau-ty we'll be - hold;

In the man - sions bright and bless - ed He'll pre - pare for us a place.
But when trav - 'ling days are o - ver Not a shad-ow, not a sigh.
Just one glimpse of Him in glo - ry Will the toils of life re-pay.
Soon the pearl - y gates will o - pen— We shall tread the streets of gold.

Chorus

When we all get to heav - en, What a day of re-
When we all What a

joic - ing that will be! When we all see
day of re - joic-ing that will be! When we all

Je - sus, We'll sing and shout the vic - to - ry.
shout, and shout the vic - to - ry.

CHORUSES

Greater Is He that Is in Me

173

Lanny Wolfe
Arr. by M. Crawford and A. Cole

Based on 1 John 4:4 and 1 Pet. 5:8

Chorus

Great-er is He that is in me, Great-er is He that is in me,

Great-er is He that is in me Than he that is in the world. Sa-tan's like a

roar-ing lion roam-ing to and fro, Seek-ing whom he may de-vour— the

Bi-ble tells us so; Man-y souls have been his prey— to fall in some weak

hour: But God has prom-ised us to-day His o-ver-com-ing pow'r.

Fine

Repeat chorus

174   I Will Call upon the Lord

Based on Psalm 18:3 and
2 Sam. 22:47

Words and Music by Michael O'Shields
Adapted by Andy Cole

Great Is the Lord

175

Psalm 48:1–2

Robert Ewing
Adapted by Andy Cole

Great is the Lord and great-ly to be prais-ed, In the

cit-y of our God, in the moun-tain of His ho-li-ness;

Beau-ti-ful for sit-u-a - tion the joy of the whole earth, Is Mount

Zi-on on the sides of the north, the cit-y of the great King.

176 Thou Art Worthy

Rev. 4:11; 5:9

Pauline M. Mills

Thou art wor-thy, Thou art wor-thy, Thou art wor-thy, O Lord,

To re-ceive glo-ry, glo-ry and hon-or, Glo-ry and

hon-or and power; For Thou hast cre-at-ed, hast all things cre-

at-ed, Thou hast cre-at-ed all things, And for Thy

pleas-ure they are cre-at-ed: Thou art wor-thy, O Lord!

Ah, Lord God

Based on Jer. 32:17–19

Kay Chance
Arr. by Eduardo Inke

Ah, Lord God, Thou hath made the heav-ens and the earth by Thy great pow-er.

Ah, Lord God, Thou hath made the heav-ens and the earth by Thine out-stretched arm.

Noth-ing is too dif-fi-cult for Thee, noth-ing is too dif-fi-cult for Thee.

Great and might-y God, great in coun-sel and might-y in deed. Noth-ing,

noth-ing, ab-so-lute-ly noth-ing, noth-ing is too dif-fi-cult for Thee.

Thy Lovingkindness

Hugh Mitchell & Jon Drevits
Based on Psalm 63:3–7

Hugh Mitchell
Arr. by Andy Cole

1. Thy lov - ing - kind - ness is bet-ter than life, Thy lov - ing -
2. Re - mem-b'ring Thee, Lord, I'm sat - is - fied, Re - mem-b'ring
3. Safe in Thy shad - ow I will— re - joice, Safe in Thy

kind - ness is bet - ter than life: My lips shall praise Thee,
Thee, Lord, I'm sat - is - fied:
shad - ow I will re - joice:

thus will I bless Thee— I will lift up my hands un - to Thy name.

Father, I Adore You

Terrye Coelho Strom
Based on John 4:23

Terrye Coelho Strom
Adapted by Andy Cole

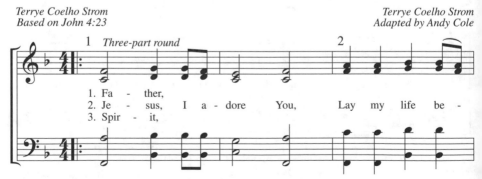

Three-part round

1. Fa - ther,
2. Je - sus, I a - dore You, Lay my life be -
3. Spir - it,

fore You, How I love You.

Sanctuary 180

John Thompson and Randy Scruggs   *John Thompson and Randy Scruggs*

Lord, pre - pare me to be a sanc - tu - ar - y, pure and

ho - ly, tried and true; with thanks - giv - ing, I'll be a

liv - ing sanc - tu - ar - y for You.

181

As the Deer

Martin Nystrom
Based on Psalm 42:1

Martin Nystrom

1. As the deer pant - eth for the wa-ter, so my soul long-eth af - ter You.
2. You're my Friend and You are my Broth-er ev-en though You are a King.

You a - lone are my heart's de - sire, and I long to wor - ship You.
I love You more than an - y oth - er, so much more than an - y - thing.

You a - lone are my strength, my shield; To You a - lone may my spir - it yield.

You a - lone are my heart's de - sire, and I long to wor - ship You.

God Can Do Anything

182

Ira Stanphill

Ira Stanphill

God can do an-y-thing, an-y-thing, an-y-thing, God can do an-y-
He can save, He can keep, He can cleanse, and He will, God can do an-y-

thing but fail;
thing but fail.

He's the Al-pha and O-me-ga, the be-gin-ning and the

end, He's the fair-est of ten-thou-sand to my soul; God can do an-y-

thing, an-y-thing, an-y-thing, God can do an-y-thing but fail.

183

God Is So Good

Unknown

African origin

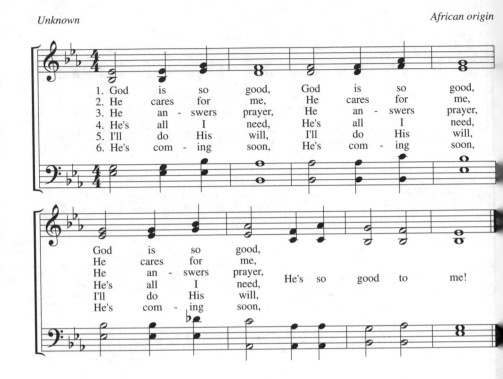

1. God is so good, God is so good,
2. He cares for me, He cares for me,
3. He an - swers prayer, He an - swers prayer,
4. He's all I need, He's all I need,
5. I'll do His will, I'll do His will,
6. He's com - ing soon, He's com - ing soon,

God is so good,
He cares for me,
He an - swers prayer,
He's all I need,
I'll do His will,
He's com - ing soon,

He's so good to me!

184

He Is Lord

Based on Phil. 2:9–11

Unknown

1. He is Lord, He is Lord, He has ris-en from the dead and He is Lord;
2. He is King, He is King, He has ris-en from the dead and He is King;

Ev - 'ry knee shall bow, ev-'ry tongue con-fess That Je - sus Christ is Lord.
Ev - 'ry knee shall bow, ev-'ry tongue con-fess That Je - sus Christ is King.

He's Able

Paul E. Raino

Paul E. Raino
Arr. by Eduardo Inke

He's a - ble, He's a - ble, I know He's a - ble, I know my Lord is

a - ble to car - ry me thru. thru. He healed the bro - ken -

heart - ed and set the cap - tive free, He made the lame to walk a - gain

and caused the blind to see; He's a - ble, He's a - ble, I know He's

a - ble, I know my Lord is a - ble to car - ry me thru.

186 His Banner over Me Is Love

B. C. Laurelton
Arr. by Andy Cole

B. C. Laurelton

His Name Is Wonderful

187

Audrey Mieir

Audrey Mieir

His name is Won-der-ful, His name is Won-der-ful, His name is
He is the might-y King, Mas-ter of ev-'ry-thing, His name is

Won-der-ful, Je-sus, my Lord; Je-sus, my Lord.

He's the great Shep-herd, the Rock of all a-ges, Al-might-y

God is He; Bow down be-fore Him, Love and a-

dore Him, His name is Won-der-ful, Je-sus, my Lord.

188

Bless the Lord, O My Soul

Unknown

Unknown
Arr. by Eduardo Inke

Bless the Lord, O my soul; Bless the Lord, O my soul;

And all that is with - in me bless His ho - ly name.

189

I Love You, Lord

Laurie Klein

Laurie Klein

I love You, Lord, and I lift my voice to wor - ship

You. O my soul, re - joice! Take joy, my King, in

what You hear; may it be a sweet, sweet sound in Your ear.

Isn't He Wonderful? **190**

Unknown

Arr. by Eduardo Inke

Is - n't He won - der - ful, won - der - ful, won - der - ful, Is - n't

Je - sus my Lord won - der - ful! Eyes have seen, ears have heard, It's re -

cord - ed in God's Word, Is - n't Je - sus my Lord won - der - ful.

Jesus, Name above All Names

Naida Hearn

Naida Hearn

Je - sus, name a - bove all names, beau-ti - ful Sav - ior, glo - ri - ous Lord. Em - man - u - el: God is with us! Bless - ed Re - deem - er, Liv - ing Word.

King of Kings

Ancient Hebrew Folksong
Arr. by Eduardo Inke

Sophie Conty and Naomi Batya

King of Kings and Lord of Lords, glo - ry, hal - le - lu - jah!

Je - sus, Prince of Peace, glo - ry, hal - le - lu - jah!

glo - ry, hal - le - lu - jah!

Let's Just Praise the Lord   **193**

Gloria and William J. Gaither   *William J. Gaither*

Let's just praise the Lord! Praise the Lord! Let's just lift our hearts to

heav - en and praise the Lord; Let's just praise the Lord! Praise the

Lord! Let's just lift our hearts to heav - en and praise the Lord!

194   Rejoice in the Lord

Ron Hamilton   *Ron Hamilton*

1. God nev-er moves with-out pur-pose or plan When try-
2. I could not see through the shad-ows a-head; So I looked
3. Now I can see test-ing comes from a-bove; God strength-

ing His ser-vant and mold-ing a man. Give thanks to the
at the cross of my Sav-ior in-stead. I bowed to the
ens His chil-dren and purg-es in love. My Fa-ther knows

Lord though your test-ing seems long; In dark-ness He giv-eth
will of the Mas-ter that day; Then peace came and tears fled
best, and I trust in His care; Through purg-ing more fruit I

Chorus

a song.
a-way.   O re-joice in the Lord. He makes no mis-take.
will bear.

He know-eth the end of each path that I take. For when I am tried and pur-i-fied, I shall come forth as gold.

Something Beautiful 195

Gloria Gaither

William J. Gaither

Some-thing beau-ti-ful, some-thing good; All my con-fu-sion He un-der-stood; All I had to of-fer Him was bro-ken-ness and strife, But He made some-thing beau-ti-ful of my life.

196 Sweet, Sweet Spirit

Doris Akers   *Doris Akers*

1. There's a sweet, sweet Spir-it in this place, And I know that
2. There are bless-ings you can-not re-ceive Till you know Him

it's the Spir-it of the Lord; There are sweet ex-pres-sions on each
in His full-ness and be-lieve; You're the one to prof-it when you

face, And I know they feel the pres-ence of the Lord.
say, "I am going to walk with Je-sus all the way."

Chorus

Sweet Ho-ly Spir-it, Sweet heav-en-ly Dove, Stay right here

with us, Fill-ing us with Your love. And for these

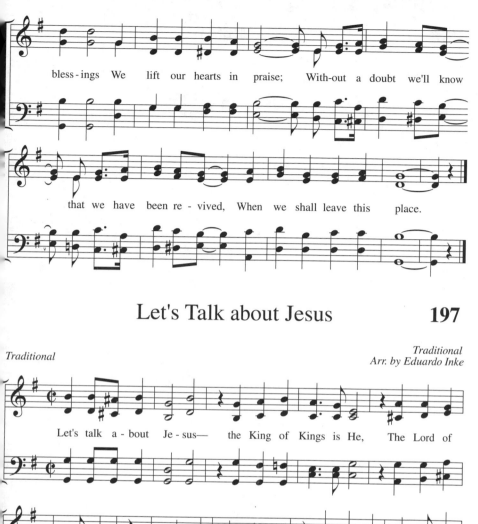

bless-ings We lift our hearts in praise; With-out a doubt we'll know

that we have been re - vived, When we shall leave this place.

Let's Talk about Jesus 197

Traditional

Traditional
Arr. by Eduardo Inke

Let's talk a - bout Je - sus— the King of Kings is He, The Lord of

Lords, su - preme through all e - ter - ni - ty; The great I AM, the Way,

the Truth, the Life, the Door— Let's talk a - bout Je - sus more and more.

198 Majesty

Jack W. Hayford   *Jack W. Hayford*

We Have Come into His House

199

Bruce Ballinger

Bruce Ballinger

1. We have come in-to His house and gath-ered in His name to wor-ship
2. Let's for-get a-bout our-selves and mag-ni-fy His name and wor-ship

Him.   We have come in-to His house and gath-ered in His name to
Him.   Let's for-get a-bout our-selves and mag-ni-fy His name and

wor-ship Him.   We have come in-to His house and gath-ered in His
wor-ship Him.   Let's for-get a-bout our-selves and mag-ni-fy His

name to wor-ship Christ the Lord.   Wor-ship Him, Christ the Lord.
name and wor-ship Christ the Lord.   Wor-ship Him, Christ the Lord.

200   Behold, What Manner of Love

Adapted by Patricia Van Tine
1 John 3:1

Patricia Van Tine

Be - hold, what man - ner of love the Fa - ther has
giv - en un - to us. Be - hold, what man - ner of
love the Fa - ther has giv - en un - to us.
That we should be called the sons of God,
That we should be called the sons of God.

He Has Made Me Glad

(I Will Enter His Gates)

201

Ps. 11:4; 118:24

Leona Von Brethorst
Arr. by Andy Cole

I will en-ter His gates with thanks-giv-ing in my heart, I will

en-ter His courts with praise; I will say, "This is the day that the

Lord has made, I will re-joice, for He has made me glad."

He has made me glad, yes, He has made me glad. I

will re-joice, for He has made me glad; made me glad.

This Is the Day

Les Garrett
Based on Ps. 118:24

Les Garrett
Arr. by Eduardo Inke

This is the day, this is the day that the Lord has made, that the Lord has made.

I will re-joice, I will re-joice and be glad in it, and be glad in it.

This is the day that the Lord has made; I will re-joice and be glad in it.

This is the day, this is the day that the Lord has made.

Happiness Is to Know the Savior 203

Ira F. Stanphill
Ira F. Stanphill
Arr. by Eduardo Inke

1. Hap-pi-ness is to know the Sav-ior, Liv-ing a life with-in His fa-vor,
2. Hap-pi-ness is a new cre-a-tion—"Je-sus and me" in close re-la-tion,
3. Hap-pi-ness is to be for-giv-en, Liv-ing a life that's worth the liv-in',

Hav-ing a change in my be-hav-ior—
Hav-ing a part in His sal-va-tion— Hap-pi-ness is the Lord;
Tak-ing a trip that leads to heav-en—

Hap-pi-ness is the Lord. Real joy is mine, no mat-ter if tear-drops

start; I've found the se-cret— it's Je-sus in my heart! Hap-pi-ness

is the Lord, Hap-pi-ness is the Lord, Hap-pi-ness is the Lord!

204   # I Just Keep Trusting My Lord

John W. Peterson

John W. Peterson
Arr. by Eduardo Inke

I just keep trust-ing my Lord   as I walk a - long,

I just keep trust-ing my Lord   and He gives a   song;   Tho the

storm-clouds dark-en the   sky   o'er the heav'n-ly   trail,   I just keep

Fine

trust-ing my Lord—   He will nev-er   fail!   He's a faith-ful   Friend,

D.S. al Fine

Such a faith-ful   Friend,   I can count on Him   to the ver-y   end;

I'm So Happy and Here's the Reason Why

205

Stanton W. Gavitt

Stanton W. Gavitt
Arr. by Eduardo Inke

I'm so hap-py and here's the rea-son why— Je-sus took my bur-den all a-way; Now I'm sing-ing as the days go by— Je-sus took my bur-den all a-way. Once my heart was heav-y with a load of sin, Je-sus took that load and gave me won-der-ful peace with-in my heart and Now I'm sing-ing as the days go by— Je-sus took my bur-den all a-way.

206 Rejoice in the Lord Always

(round)

Unknown
Arr. by Eduardo Inke

Phil. 4:4

1. Re - joice in the Lord al - ways, and a - gain I say re - joice,

2. Re - joice in the Lord al - ways, and a - gain I say re - joice,

3. Re - joice, re - joice, and a - gain I say re - joice;

4. Re - joice, re - joice, and a - gain I say re - joice.

Peace Like a River

Unknown   *Unknown*

1. I've got peace like a riv - er, I've got peace like a
2. I've got love like an o - cean, I've got love like an
3. I've got joy like a foun - tain, I've got joy like a

riv - er, I've got peace like a riv - er in my soul, I've got
o - cean, I've got love like an o - cean in my soul, I've got
foun - tain, I've got joy like a foun - tain in my soul, I've got

peace like a riv - er, I've got peace like a riv - er,
love like an o - cean, I've got love like an o - cean,
joy like a foun - tain, I've got joy like a foun - tain,

I've got peace like a riv - er in my soul. (my soul.)
I've got love like an o - cean in my soul. (my soul.)
I've got joy like a foun - tain in my soul. (my soul.)

208 Unto Thee, O Lord

Charles F. Monroe

Charles F. Monroe
Arr. by Eduardo Inke

O my God, I trust in Thee;

God, I trust in Thee; Let me not be a-shamed,

let not mine en - e - mies tri-umph ov - er me.

Be Still and Know 209

Ps. 46:10; Exod. 15:26

Unknown

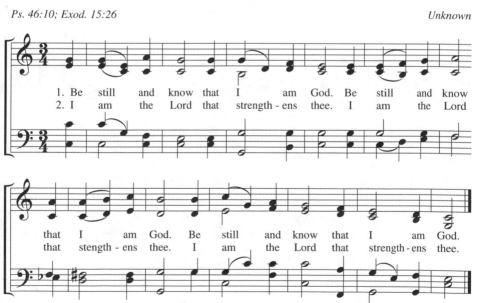

1. Be still and know that I am God. Be still and know
2. I am the Lord that strength-ens thee. I am the Lord

that I am God. Be still and know that I am God.
that stength-ens thee. I am the Lord that strength-ens thee.

210   They That Wait upon the Lord

Isa. 40:31
Stuart Hamblen

Stuart Hamblen
Adapted by Andy Cole

They that wait up-on the Lord shall re - new their strength; They shall mount up with wings like ea - gles; They shall run, and not be wea - ry; They shall walk, and not faint. Teach me, Lord, teach me, Lord, to wait.

Gentle Shepherd

211

Gloria Gaither

William J. Gaither

Gen - tle Shep - herd, come and lead us, For we need You to help us find our way. Gen - tle Shep-herd, come and feed us, For we need Your strength from day to day. There's no oth - er we can turn to Who can help us face an - oth - er day; Gen - tle Shep-herd, come and lead us For we need You to help us find our way.

212

Lord, I Need You

Ron Hamilton

Ron Hamilton

1. Some - times when life seems gen - tle and bless - ings flood my way, I
2. Lord, help me to re - mem - ber I'm weak but You are strong. I

turn my gaze a - way from You and soon for - get to pray. But
can - not sing a - part from You, for Lord, You are my song. Al -

when the sky grows dark - er and cour - age turns to fear, My
though I'm prone to wan - der and boast in all I do, Lord,

anx - ious voice cries up - ward with words You long to hear.
keep my eyes turned up - ward so I de - pend on You.

Chorus

Lord, I need You when the sea of life is calm. O Lord, I need

You when the wind is blow-ing strong. Wheth-er tri - als come or cease,

keep me al - ways on my knees. Lord, I need You. Lord, I need You.

Cares Chorus 213

Kelly Willard

Kelly Willard

I cast all my cares up - on You. I lay all of my

bur - dens down at Your feet. And an - y time that I don't know

what to do, I will cast all my cares up - on You.

214

Into My Heart

Harry D. Clarke

Harry D. Clarke

In - to my heart, in - to my heart, Come in - to my heart, Lord Je - sus:

Come in to - day, Come in to stay, Come in - to my heart, Lord Je - sus.

215

Jesus, Lord to Me

G. McS., G. N.

Gary McSpadden, Greg Nelson

Je - sus, Je - sus, Lord to me; Mas - ter, Sav - ior, Prince of

Peace! Ru - ler of my heart to - day, Je - sus, Lord to me.

Lord, I Want to Be a Christian

Spiritual   *Spiritual*

1. Lord, I want to be a Chris-tian In-a my heart, in-a my heart, Lord, I want to be a Chris-tian In-a my heart.
2. Lord, I want to be more lov-ing In-a my heart, in-a my heart, Lord, I want to be more lov-ing In-a my heart.
3. Lord, I want to be more ho-ly In-a my heart, in-a my heart, Lord, I want to be more ho-ly In-a my heart.
4. Lord, I want to be like Je-sus In-a my heart, in-a my heart, Lord, I want to be like Je-sus In-a my heart.

Refrain

In-a my heart, In-a my heart, In-a my heart, In-a my heart,

Lord, I want to be a Chris-tian In-a my heart.
Lord, I want to be more lov-ing In-a my heart.
Lord, I want to be more ho-ly In-a my heart.
Lord, I want to be like Je-sus In-a my heart.

217

Open Our Eyes

Bob Cull   *Bob Cull*

O - pen our eyes, Lord, we want to see Je - sus,

To reach out and touch Him and say that we love Him;

O - pen our ears, Lord, and help us to lis - ten,

O - pen our eyes, Lord; we want to see Je - sus.

Beloved, Let Us Love One Another 218

1 John 4:7–8

Unknown

Be - lov-ed, let us love one an - oth-er,

For love is of God; and ev - 'ry - one that lov - eth is

born of God, and know - eth God; He that lov - eth not,

know-eth not God, for God is love, So be - lov-ed

Optional Ending

let us love one an - oth - er. (First John, four sev - en and eight.)

219 # The Family of God

William J. & Gloria Gaither

William J. Gaither

1. You will no - tice we say bro - ther and sis - ter 'round
2. From the door of an orph-'nage to the house of the

here. It's be - cause we're a fam - 'ly and these folks are so near. When
King, No long - er an out - cast, a new song I sing; From

one has a heart - ache we all share the tears, And re -
rags un - to rich - es, from the weak to the strong, I'm not

joice in each vic - t'ry in this fam - 'ly so dear.
wor - thy to be here, but praise God I be - long!

Refrain

I'm so glad I'm a part of the fam - 'ly of God; I've been washed in the

foun - tain, Cleansed by His blood! Joint heirs with Je - sus as we tra - vel this sod, For I'm part of the fam - 'ly, the fam - 'ly of God.

The Old-Time Religion 220

Unknown

Unknown
Adapted by Andy Cole

Chorus:	*Give me that old - time re - lig - ion,*				*Give me that old - time re -*		
1.	It	was good	for our	moth - ers,	It	was good	for our
2.	Makes	me love	ev - 'ry - bod - y,		Makes	me love	ev - 'ry-
3.	It	was good	for our	fath - ers,	It	was good	for our
4.	It	can take us	all to	heav - en,	It	can take us	all to

lig - ion, Give me that old - time re - lig - ion, It's good e-nough for me.
moth-ers, It was good for our moth-ers, It's good e-nough for me.
bod - y, Makes me love ev - 'ry-bod - y, It's good e-nough for me.
fath - ers, It was good for our fath-ers, It's good e-nough for me.
heav - en, It can take us all to heav-en, It's good e-nough for me.*

*Repeat chorus after last verse.

221   The Law of the Lord

Ps. 19:7–10

Unknown
Adapted by Andy Cole

1. The law of the Lord is per - fect, con - vert-ing the soul; The tes - ti - mon - y of the Lord is sure, mak-ing wise the sim-ple.
2. The stat-utes of the Lord are right, re - joic-ing the heart; — The com - mand - ment of the Lord is pure, en - light - 'ning the eyes.
3. The fear of the Lord is clean, en - dur-ing for - ev - er; — The judg - ments of the Lord are true, and right-eous all to - geth-er.

Chorus

More to be de - sired are they than gold, yea, than much fine gold; Sweet - er al - so than hon - ey and the hon - ey - comb.

More - o - ver by them is thy ser - vant warned, is thy ser - vant warned; And in keep-ing of them there is great re - ward.

D.S. al Fine on final chorus

Thy Word Have I Hid in My Heart 222

Ps. 119:11
Ernest O. Sellers

Ernest O. Sellers

Thy Word have I hid in my heart That I might not sin a-gainst Thee;

That I might not sin, that I might not sin, Thy Word have I hid in my heart.

For God So Loved the World 223

Frances Townsend
Based on John 3:16

Alfred B. Smith
Arr. by Eduardo Inke

For God so loved the world, He gave His on-ly Son, To die on

Cal-v'ry's tree, From sin to set me free; Some day He's com-ing

back, What glo-ry that will be! Won-der-ful His love to me.

Everybody Ought to Know

Unknown   *Unknown*

He's the fair - est;
D.S. al Fine

thou - sand; Ev - 'ry - bod - y ought to know.

Alleluia

225

Jerry Sinclair

Jerry Sinclair
Adapted by Andy Cole

*Add descant 2nd time through

Christ was born to die on Cal-va-ry To re-deem all lost hu-man-i-ty.

Al-le - lu - ia, Al-le-lu - ia, Al - le-lu-ia, Al-le-lu - ia,

Con-q'ring death He a-rose tri-um-phant-ly. Now He reigns for all e-ter-ni-ty.

Al-le - lu-ia, Al-le-lu - ia, Al - le-lu-ia, Al-le-lu - ia!

226   Go, Tell It on the Mountains

American Folksong
Arr. by Andy Cole

John W. Work

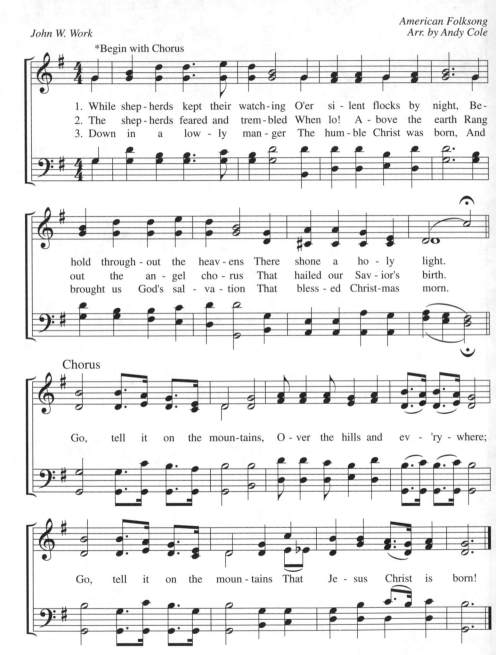

*Begin with Chorus

1. While shep-herds kept their watch-ing O'er si-lent flocks by night, Be-
2. The shep-herds feared and trem-bled When lo! A-bove the earth Rang
3. Down in a low-ly man-ger The hum-ble Christ was born, And

hold through-out the heav-ens There shone a ho-ly light.
out the an-gel cho-rus That hailed our Sav-ior's birth.
brought us God's sal-va-tion That bless-ed Christ-mas morn.

Chorus

Go, tell it on the moun-tains, O-ver the hills and ev-'ry-where;

Go, tell it on the moun-tains That Je-sus Christ is born!

I Will Sing of the Mercies of the Lord   227

Ps. 89:1

James H. Fillmore

I will sing of the mer-cies of the Lord for-ev-er, I will sing, I will sing,

I will sing of the mer-cies of the Lord for-ev-er, I will sing of the mer-cies of the Lord.

With my   mouth will I make known Thy faith-ful-ness, Thy faith-ful-ness, With my

mouth will I make known Thy faith-ful-ness to all gen-er - a - tions.

228   O How He Loves You and Me

Kurt Kaiser

Kurt Kaiser
Arr. by Andy Cole

1. O how He loves you and me.   O how He
2. Je - sus to Cal - vary did go,   His love for

loves you and me;   He gave His life,   what
man - kind to show;   What He did there   brought

more could He give: O how He loves you,   O how He
hope from de - spair:

loves me, O how He loves you and me.

The Lord Is Good

229

Alfred B. Smith

Alfred B. Smith
Arr. by Andy Cole

The Lord is good Tell it wher-ev-er you go, The
Lord is good Tell it that oth-ers may know; Tell of His
bless-ings and tell of His love, Tell how He's com-ing from heav-en a-
bove: The Lord is good Tell it wher-ev-er you go!

230
Seek Ye First

Matt. 6:33; 7:7

Karen Lafferty

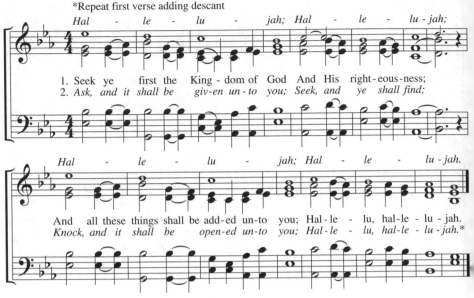

1. Seek ye first the King-dom of God And His right-eous-ness;
2. Ask, and it shall be giv-en un-to you; Seek, and ye shall find;

And all these things shall be add-ed un-to you; Hal-le - lu, hal-le - lu - jah.
Knock, and it shall be open-ed un-to you; Hal-le - lu, hal-le - lu - jah.*

231
Lord, Be Glorified

Bob Kilpatrick — Bob Kilpatrick

1. In my life, Lord, be glor - i - fied, be glor - i - fied.
2. In our home, Lord, be glor - i - fied, be glor - i - fied.
3. In Your church, Lord, be glor - i - fied, be glor - i - fied.

In my life, Lord, be glor - i - fied to - day.
In our home, Lord, be glor - i - fied to - day.
In Your church, Lord, be glor - i - fied to - day.

Make Me a Servant

232

Kelly Willard

Kelly Willard

Make me a ser-vant, hum-ble and meek; Lord, let me lift up those who are weak; And may the pray'r of my heart al-ways be: Make me a ser-vant, make me a ser-vant, make me a ser-vant to-day.

Learning to Lean

233

John Stallings

John Stallings

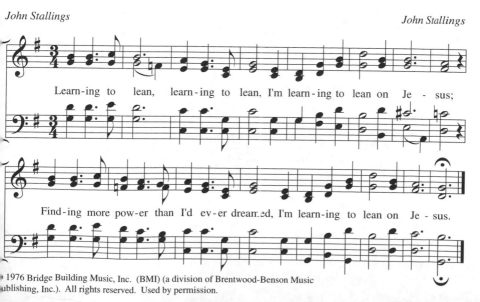

Learn-ing to lean, learn-ing to lean, I'm learn-ing to lean on Je-sus; Find-ing more pow-er than I'd ev-er dreamed, I'm learn-ing to lean on Je-sus.

234

I'll Fly Away

Albert E. Brumley
Arr. by Greg Soule

Albert E. Brumley

1. Some glad morn-ing when this life is o'er, I'll fly a-
2. Just a few more wea-ry days and then, I'll fly a-

way; (in the morn-ing;) To a home on God's ce-les-tial shore,
way; (in the morn-ing;) To a land where joys shall nev-er end,

Chorus

I'll fly a-way. I'll fly a-way, O glo-ry,

I'll fly a-way; (in the morn-ing;) When I die, hal-le

lu-jah by and by, I'll fly a-way.

I've Got a Mansion

(Mansion Over the Hilltop)

235

Ira F. Stanphill

Ira F. Stanphill

1. I'm sat - is - fied with just a cot - tage be - low, A lit - tle sil - ver
2. Tho' oft - en tempt - ed, tor - ment - ed and test - ed And like the proph - et
3. Don't think me poor or de - sert - ed or lone - ly, I'm not dis - cour - aged,

and a lit - tle gold; But in that cit - y where the ran - somed will shine,
my pil - low a stone; And tho' I find here no per - ma - nent dwell - ing,
I'm heav - en bound; I'm just a pil - grim in search of a cit - y.

Chorus

I want a gold one that's sil - ver lined.
I know He'll give me a man - sion my own. I've got a man - sion just
I want a man - sion, a harp and a crown.

o - ver the hill - top, In that bright land where we'll nev - er grow old; And some day

yon - der we will nev - er more wan - der But walk the streets that are pur - est gold.

236 What a Day That Will Be

Jim Hill   *Jim Hill*

1. There is com - ing a day when no heart-aches shall come,
2. There'll be no sor-row there, no more bur - dens to bear,

No more clouds in the sky, no more tears to dim the eye; All is
No more sick - ness, no pain, no more part-ing o - ver there; And for-

peace for ev - er - more on that hap - py gold-en shore— What a day,
ev - er I will be with the One Who died for me— What a day,

glo - ri - ous day, that will be.
glo - ri - ous day, that will be.

Chorus

What a day that will be when my

Je - sus I shall see, And I look up - on His face— the One Who

saved me by His grace; When He takes me by the hand, and leads me

through the Promised Land, What a day, glo-ri-ous day, that will be.

This World Is Not My Home   237

Unknown   *Unknown*
Arr. by Vernon Whaley

This world is not my home I'm just a-pass-ing through. My trea-sures are laid

up Some-where be-yond the blue. The an-gels beck-on me From heav-en's o-pen

Fine

door, And I can't feel at home in this world an-y-more. O Lord, You know

O Lord, You know

D.S. al Fine

I have no friend like You. If heav-en's not my home, Then Lord, what will I do?

238

Until Then

Stuart Hamblen   *Stuart Hamblen*

1. My heart can sing when I pause to re - mem - ber
2. The things of earth will dim and lose their val - ue,
3. This wea - ry world with all its toil and strug - gle

A heart - ache here is but a step - ping stone
If we re - call, they're bor - rowed for a - while;
May take its toll of mis - er - y and strife;

A - long a trail that's wind - ing al - ways up - ward—
And things of earth that cause the heart to trem - ble,
The soul of man is like a wait - ing fal - con—

This trou - bled world is not my fi - nal home.
Re - mem - bered there, will on - ly bring a smile.
When it's re - leased, it's des - tined for the skies.

Refrain

But un - til then my heart will go on sing - ing, Un - til

then with joy I'll car-ry on— Un-til the day my eyes be-hold the cit-y, Un-til the day God calls me home.

What a Mighty God We Serve 239

Unknown
Arr. by Greg Soule

Unknown

What a might-y God we serve. What a might-y God we serve. An-gels bow be-fore Him, heav'n and earth a-dore Him; What a might-y God we serve.

240
I Will Serve Thee

William J. and Gloria Gaither   *William J. Gaither*

Lyrics:

1. I will serve Thee be-cause I love Thee;
2. I was noth-ing be-fore You found me;

You have giv-en life to me.

You have giv-en life to me.

Heart-aches, bro-ken piec-es, Ru-ined lives are why You died on Cal-vary. Your touch was what I longed for; You have giv-en life to me.

I Am Crucified with Christ

241

John G. Elliott
Based on Gal. 2:20

John G. Elliott

242

Isn't He?

John Wimber   *John Wimber*

1. Is - n't He beau - ti - ful? Beau - ti - ful, is - n't He?
2. Is - n't He won - der - ful? Won - der - ful, is - n't He?

Prince of Peace, Son of God, is - n't He?

Coun - sel - or, Al - might - y God, is-n't He, is - n't He, is-n't He?

America the Beautiful 243

Katharine Lee Bates   *Samuel A. Ward*

1. O beau - ti - ful for spa - cious skies, For am - ber waves of grain, For pur - ple moun-tain maj - es - ties A - bove the fruit-ed plain! A - mer - i - ca! A - mer - i - ca! God shed His grace on thee, And crown thy good with broth - er - hood From sea to shin-ing sea.

2. O beau - ti - ful for pil - grim feet, Whose stern, im - pas - sioned stress A thor-ough-fare for free - dom beat A - cross the wil-der-ness! A - mer - i - ca! A - mer - i - ca! God mend thine ev - 'ry flaw, Con - firm thy soul in self-con-trol, Thy lib - er - ty in law.

3. O beau - ti - ful for he - roes proved In lib - er - at - ing strife, Who more than self their coun - try loved And mer - cy more than life! A - mer - i - ca! A - mer - i - ca! May God thy gold re - fine, Till all suc - cess be no - ble-ness, And ev - 'ry gain di - vine.

4. O beau - ti - ful for pa - triot dream That sees be - yond the years, Thine al - a - bas - ter cit - ies gleam—Un - dimmed by hu - man tears! A - mer - i - ca! A - mer - i - ca! God shed His grace on thee, And crown thy good with broth - er - hood From sea to shin-ing sea.

244

The Star-Spangled Banner

Francis Scott Key   *John Stafford Smith*

1. O   say! can you   see,   by the dawn's ear - ly   light,
2. On the shore, dim - ly   seen through the mists of   the   deep,
3. O   thus be   it   ev - er when free men shall stand

What so proud - ly we   hailed at the   twi - light's last   gleam-ing?
Where the foe's haugh - ty   host in dread   si - lence re - pos - es,
Be - tween their loved homes and the   war's des - o - la - tion!

Whose broad stripes and bright   stars, through the   per - i - lous   fight
What is   that which the   breeze,   o'er the   tow - er - ing   steep,
Blest with vic - t'ry and   peace,   may the heav'n - res - cued   land

O'er the ram - parts we watched, were so   gal - lant - ly stream - ing?
As   it   fit - ful - ly   blows, half con - ceals, half dis - clos - es?
Praise the Pow'r that hath made   and pre - served us   a   na - tion!

245   My Country, 'Tis of Thee

Samuel Francis Smith

From Thesaurus Musicus

1. My coun-try, 'tis of thee, Sweet land of lib-er-ty,
Of thee I sing: Land where my fa-thers died, Land of the
pil-grim's pride, From ev-'ry moun-tain-side Let free-dom ring!

2. My na-tive coun-try, thee, Land of the no-ble free,
Thy name I love: I love thy rocks and rills, Thy woods and
tem-pled hills; My heart with rap-ture thrills Like that a-bove.

3. Let mu-sic swell the breeze, And ring from all the trees
Sweet free-dom's song: Let mor-tal tongues a-wake, Let all that
breathe par-take; Let rocks their si-lence break, The sound pro-long.

4. Our fa-ther's God, to Thee, Au-thor of lib-er-ty,
To Thee we sing: Long may our land be bright With free-dom's
ho-ly light; Pro-tect us by Thy might, Great God, our King!

INDEX OF HYMNS